pages
54
206
81
38

The American Singer

The American Singer

✪ ✪ BOOK SIX ✪ ✪

John W. Beattie
DEAN, THE SCHOOL OF MUSIC, NORTHWESTERN UNIVERSITY
EVANSTON, ILLINOIS

Josephine Wolverton
ASSISTANT SUPERVISOR, EVANSTON SCHOOLS
ASSISTANT PROFESSOR, THE SCHOOL OF MUSIC, NORTHWESTERN UNIVERSITY
EVANSTON, ILLINOIS

Grace V. Wilson
DIRECTOR OF MUSIC, PUBLIC SCHOOLS, WICHITA, KANSAS

Howard Hinga
ASSISTANT DIRECTOR OF MUSIC, PUBLIC SCHOOLS
INSTRUCTOR OF PUBLIC SCHOOL MUSIC, EASTMAN SCHOOL OF MUSIC
ROCHESTER, NEW YORK

✪ ✪ ✪

American Book Company

NEW YORK	CINCINNATI	CHICAGO

BOSTON	ATLANTA	DALLAS	SAN FRANCISCO

Beattie and others, The American Singer, Book Six

E. P. 7

Made in U. S. A.

To the Boys and Girls

During the past thirty years there have been such developments in means of transportation and communication that today all the peoples of the world are neighbors. An ocean trip to Europe was once a great adventure; today an airplane can fly around the earth in less time than it takes a ship to cross the Atlantic. News of events in distant countries reaches us by radio in a matter of minutes. We in America live at the crossroads of the world and must learn to know other peoples and their cultures.

In this book you will learn some unusual music from distant places as well as many songs of the Americas. You will be interested in comparing the rhythmic and melodic structure of this material, which is representative of many peoples.

You will also do more singing with words at sight, encounter new rhythmic patterns such as syncopation, continue singing with orchestral accompaniment, and begin to sing in three parts. All these activities will add to your pleasure in making and listening to music.

Acknowledgments

Grateful acknowledgment is made to publishers, authors, and individuals for permission to reprint the following material used in this book:

"The Mist and All" by Dixie Willson.
"Roundup Lullaby" from *Sun and Saddle Leather* by Badger Clark, Chapman and Grimes.
"Freight Boats" from *I Go A-Traveling* and "The New Highway" from *A World to Know,* both by James Tippett, Harper and Bros.
"Spring Song" from *City Pastorals* by William Griffith, J. T. White & Co.
"Kuckaburro," Janet Tobin, collector.
"Song of the Infant Jesus" and "The Shepherdess" from materials recorded by the Institute of Folklore Investigations, University of Chile, Eugenio Pereira Salas, editor.
"Thunderdrums" and "Double Bear Dances" from *The Box of God* and "The Blue Duck" from *Many, Many Moons* by Lew Sarett, Henry Holt and Co.
"The Crab" (O Caranguejo), "The Ship from Heaven" (Vamos Maninha), "In the Early Morning" (Acordei de Madrugada), "In Bahia" (Na Bahia Tem), "Flying Down to Rio" (Manda, tiro, tiro la) from the *Practical Guide,* edited by Heitor Villa-Lobos for the Ministry of Education, Brazil.
"Villancico" collected by Carlos Vega and harmonized by Sylvia Eisenstein.
"Maranoa Lullaby" from *Aboriginal Songs of Australia,* arranged by H. O. Lethbridge, G. Schirmer, Inc.
"The Legend of St. Nicolas," Susanne Bloch, collector.

We are also indebted to the following for contributing and translating the following:

Armen Tosoonian for the Armenian "Cradle Song;" George Radakovich for the Serbian "O'er the Horizon;" Timothy Fetler for Latvian, Russian, and Ukrainian songs; Milton Brazda for Czech and Slovak songs; Luisa Bardas for Italian songs; Constance Hatges for Greek songs; Chi Tung Tsu for the Chinese "Farmer's Song;" Captain Richard Park and Nahundu Dotta-Majunder for the Bengali "Song of the Pigeon."

We are likewise indebted for the following contributions:

Major Adelbert Huguelet for the Papuan "Mafulu War Song;" Mercedes Navarro Cameron for the Panamanian "The Little Sailboat;" Fred H. Bloch for songs of Incaic origin; Dorothy Brown and W. C. Lanton for research in the field of Negro spirituals; Mr. and Mrs. Charles Seeger for research in the field of American folk songs and games; Elizabeth Waterman for her continuing help with our rhythm program; and Harold M. Johnson for the orchestrations.

ILLUSTRATIONS BY CORINNE BOYD DILLON, JANET SMALLEY, JEANNE MacLAVY

The American Singer
BOOK SIX

God of Our Fathers

Daniel C. Roberts   ROTE   George W. Warren

Majestically

Trumpets

1. God of our fa - thers,
2. Thy love di - vine hath
3. Re - fresh Thy peo - ple

Whose al - might - y hand
led us in the past,
on their toil - some way,

Leads forth in
In this free
Lead us from

beau - ty all the star - ry band
land by Thee our lot is cast;
night to nev - er - end - ing day;

Of shin - ing worlds in splen - dor thro' the skies,
Be Thou our rul - er, guard - ian, guide and stay,
Fill all our lives with love and grace di - vine,

Our grate - ful songs be - fore Thy throne a - rise.
Thy word our law, Thy paths our cho - sen way.
And glo - ry, laud, and praise be ev - er Thine.

B-flat trumpets play their parts in the key of F, one step higher than the notes are printed. The class sings in the key of E flat, the key in which the hymn is printed.

(9)

Autumn Holiday

Paraphrased   ROTE   Hugo Wolf

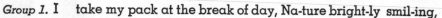

Joyfully

Group 1. I take my pack at the break of day, Na-ture bright-ly smil-ing,

O'er the wood - ed hills I go mer-ri-ly on my way.

Group 2. Strid-ing forth o'er hill and plain, I pass thro' woods and

louder

mead - ows show - ing Au-tumn col - ors bright-ly glow - ing,

Mak-ing all a par - a - dise on earth be - low.

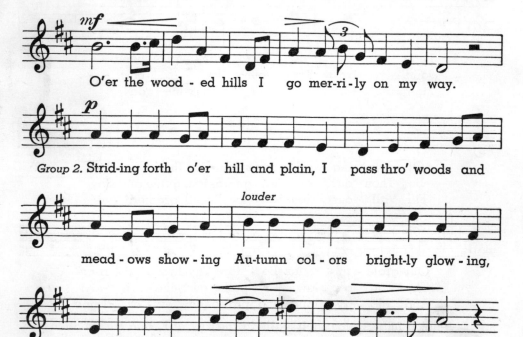

(10)

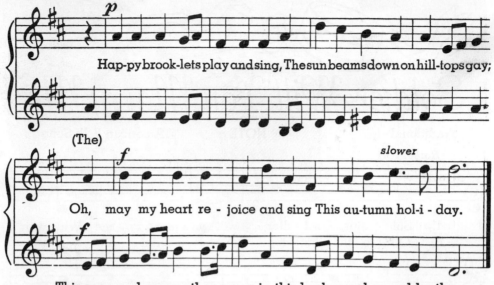

Hap-py brook-lets play and sing, The sun beams down on hill-tops gay;

(The)

Oh, may my heart re - joice and sing This au-tumn hol-i - day.

This song and many other songs in this book may be used by the special school choir.

Good Night

Traditional   ROTE   **Old Round**

Slowly and smoothly

1

Good night to you all, and sweet be your sleep!

2

May an - gels a - round you their si - lent watch keep!

3

Good night, good night, good night, good night!

Soldier, Will You Marry Me

Traditional   NOTE   American Folk Song

Rather fast

1. "Sol - dier, sol - dier, will you mar - ry me With your mus - ket, fife, and drum?" "How can I mar - ry such a pret - ty lit - tle girl When I have no hat to put on?"

2. Off to the hat - ter she did go As hard as she could run, Brought him back the fin - est that was there. "Now, sol - dier, put it on."

3. "Soldier, soldier, will you marry me
With your musket, fife, and drum?"
"How can I marry such a pretty little girl
When I have no coat to put on?"

4. Off to the tailor she did go
As hard as she could run,
Brought him back the finest that was there.
"Now, soldier, put it on."

5. "Soldier, soldier, will you marry me
With your musket, fife, and drum?"
"How can I marry such a pretty little girl
When I have no shoes to put on?"

6. Off to the shoe shop she did go
   As hard as she could run,
   Brought him back the finest that were there.
   "Now, soldier, put them on."

7. "Soldier, soldier, will you marry me
   With your musket, fife, and drum?"
   "How can I marry such a pretty little girl
   With a wife and child at home?"

The Mist and All

Dixie Willson   ROTE   Frédéric Chopin

Lightly

1. I like the fall, the mist and all, I like the night owl's
2. I like the gray No - vem - ber day And bare, dead boughs that

lone - ly call And wail - ing sound of wind a - round, —
cold - ly sway A - gainst my pane, I like the rain, —

slower

1. And wail-ing sound a - round. 2. A-gainst my pane, I like the rain.

Fairest Lord Jesus

Unknown   NOTE   Silesian Folk Song

Reverently

1. Fair - est Lord Je - sus, Rul - er of all na - ture,
2. Fair are the mead - ows, Fair - er still the wood - lands,
3. Fair is the sun - shine, Fair - er still the moon - light

1. Rul - er of na - ture,
2. Fair - er the wood - lands,
3. Fair - er the moon - light,

O Thou of God and man the Son,
Robed in the bloom - ing garb of spring;
And all the twin - kling star - ry host;

Thee will I cher - ish, Thee will I hon - or,
Je - sus is fair - er, Je - sus is pur - er,
Je - sus shines bright - er, Je - sus shines pur - er

Turn to page 233 for orchestra parts.

Thou, my soul's glo - ry, joy, and crown.
Who makes the woe - ful heart to sing.
Than all the an - gels heav'n can boast.

A flat placed before a note lowers the tone one half step.

This hymn is known in many lands as the "Crusaders' Hymn."
The crusaders are said to have sung it in their expeditions to the
Holy Land.

Lovely Evening

Traditional   NOTE   Old Round
In strict time

Oh, how love - ly is the eve - ning, is the eve - ning,

When the bells are sweet - ly ring - ing, sweet - ly ring - ing,

Ding dong ding dong ding dong!

Abide With Me

Henry Lyte   NOTE   William H. Monk

Reverently

1. A - bide with me, fast falls the e - ven - tide;
2. Swift to its close ebbs out life's lit - tle day;
3. I need Thy pres - ence ev - 'ry pass - ing hour;

The dark-ness deep- ens, Lord, with me a - bide!
Earth's joys grow dim, its glo - ries pass a - way;
What but Thy grace can foil the tempt - er's pow'r?

When oth - er help - ers fail, and com - forts flee,
Change and de - cay in all a-round I see;
Who, like Thy - self, my guide and stay can be?

Help of the help-less, oh, a - bide with me!
Oh, Thou Who chang-eth not, a - bide with me!
Thro' cloud and sun-shine, Lord, a - bide with me!

A natural (♮) before a note in a song with a flat key signature
raises the tone one half step. If *do*, for instance, has a natural sign
before it, call the note *di*.

The Good Comrade

Paraphrased   NOTE   German Marching Song
(1825)

Steadily

1. I had a boy-hood com-rade, the best of friends was he;
2. In time of war, to-geth-er we saw the bat-tles thro';

When drums of war were call - ing,
So now what-e'er be - tide me,

And men in line were fall - ing,
He'll al - ways walk be - side me,

He marched in step with me, He marched in step with me.
My com-rade, good and true; My com - rade, good and true.

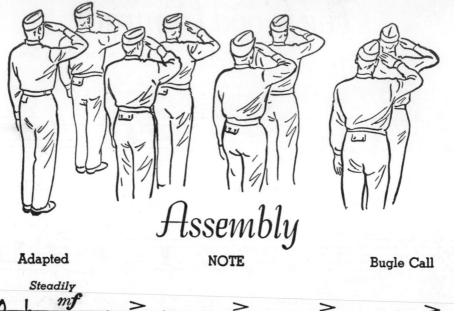

Assembly

Adapted · NOTE · Bugle Call

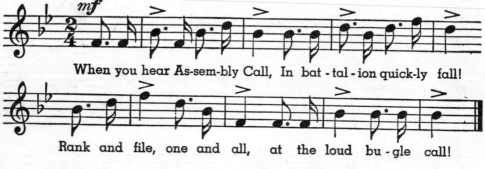

Steadily
mf

When you hear As-sem-bly Call, In bat-tal-ion quick-ly fall!

Rank and file, one and all, at the loud bu-gle call!

B-flat trumpets play each note one step higher:

etc.

Clap the rhythms, accenting the first note after each bar:

Taps

Adapted   NOTE   Bugle Call

Slowly

Far a - way,   bu-gles play,   Sound - ing

Far a - way,   —   bu-gles play,   —

taps   for the close   of the   day;   Night's be-

of the day;

gun, gone the   sun, Day   is done.

Night's be - gun, gone the   sun, Day   is done.

"Taps" sounds well when it is played by two B-flat trumpets.

(19)

Reveille

Adapted   NOTE   Bugle Call

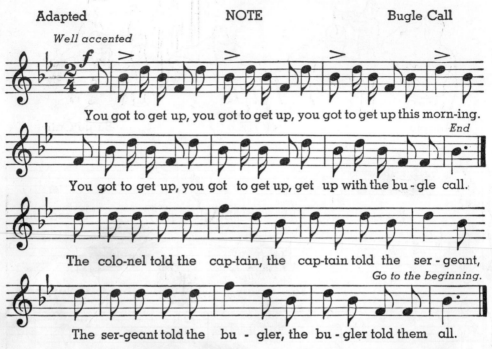

You got to get up, you got to get up, you got to get up this morn-ing.

You got to get up, you got to get up, get up with the bu-gle call.

The colo-nel told the cap-tain, the cap-tain told the ser-geant,

The ser-geant told the bu-gler, the bu-gler told them all.

In most songs that you have sung, the strongest accent falls on the first note after each bar. Try a new pattern, in which the accent falls on the second and fourth beats. In this kind of pattern we stress the *after beat.* Clap the patterns below:

Standard accents:

After-beat accents:

1. Clap a phrase of standard accents; then clap a phrase of after-beat accents, using the measures in A above.
2. Divide the class into two groups. One group claps standard accents while at the same time the other group claps after-beat accents. Change groups occasionally.
3. Clap the patterns in B above.
4. In practicing the after-beat pattern, step on the unaccented beats and stand still and clap on the accented beats. Change groups.

On Patrol

Translated   ROTE   French Soldiers' Song

In strict time

Once there was a squad of four
They were find-ing life a bore

One, two, one, two, one, two, One, two,   two,
Chant, do not sing.

Drill-ing for a cor-po-ral.
In a march con-tin-u-al.   Said the first,

two,   two,   One, two, one, two, One, two,

"It's get-ting wet-ter;" said the sec-ond, "That's the rain."

two,   two,   two,

Third one cried, "It's nev-er bet-ter;" fourth re-plied, "But why com-plain?"

two,   two,   two,   two,

The cor-p'ral said, "This is the way! When it rains, for you it's

two,   two,   two,   two,   two,

Wa-a-a-a-a-a-a-a-a-a-ash-ing day!

two,   two,   One, two, one, two, one, two, one, two,

Move a-long, my lit-tle troop, Keep stir-ring the soup, stir-ring the

One, two,   two,   two,   two,

soup! Move a-long, my lit-tle troop, Keep stir-ring the soup, keep stir-ring the

two, two, two, two,

soup!"

two, One, two, one, two, one, two, Halt!

There are both standard accents and after-beat accents in this song:

Standard accent:

After-beat accents:

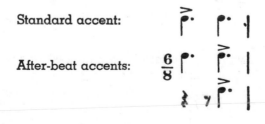

Reuben Ranzo

Traditional   NOTE   Sailor Chantey

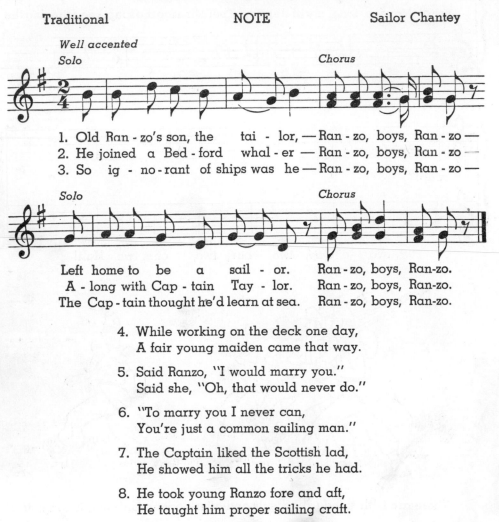

1. Old Ran - zo's son, the   tai - lor, — Ran - zo, boys, Ran - zo —
2. He joined a Bed - ford   whal - er — Ran - zo, boys, Ran - zo —
3. So ig - no - rant of ships was he — Ran - zo, boys, Ran - zo —

Left home to be   a   sail - or.   Ran - zo, boys, Ran - zo.
A - long with Cap - tain Tay - lor.   Ran - zo, boys, Ran - zo.
The Cap - tain thought he'd learn at sea. Ran - zo, boys, Ran - zo.

4. While working on the deck one day,
   A fair young maiden came that way.

5. Said Ranzo, "I would marry you."
   Said she, "Oh, that would never do."

6. "To marry you I never can,
   You're just a common sailing man."

7. The Captain liked the Scottish lad,
   He showed him all the tricks he had.

8. He took young Ranzo fore and aft,
   He taught him proper sailing craft.

9. To be a skipper Ranzo came,
   The Captain's daughter took his name.

This ballad with slight alterations in the text was written down by James Taft Hatfield on one of the last of the three-masted sailing vessels, which sailed from Pensacola, Florida, to Nice, France, in 1886. The trip took eighty-four days.

Indian Summer

Mabel Cobb   ROTE   Grace V. Wilson

An In - dian on a lone - ly hill, ar - rayed in buck - skin trap-ping, Is stir - ring in the gen - tle breeze; his time has come for nap-ping. His moc - ca - sins are green and brown with bronze and am - ber bead - ing; A - bove his garb a blan - ket blows of pat - terned scar - let weav-ing. The feath - ers round his nod - ding head are tint - ed gold and yel - low; And though his wraps are brave in hue, he sits sub - dued and mel - low.

The One-Tune Piper

Adapted
In strict time

NOTE

French Folk Song
from Languedoc

1. Long a - go an a - ged pip-er tramped the coun-try up and down,
2. Once a stran-ger asked the pip-er if an - oth - er tune he'd play;

You could hear his wail-ing tune in ev - 'ry fair and mar-ket town:
Said the pip-er, "I keep blow-ing just the same one ev - 'ry day:

mi mi do mi mi do ti do re do ti la si,

Ev - er gay and ev - er spright - ly in a mi - nor mel - o - dy.
It was made by my grand - fa - ther and it's good e - nough for me."

Sing Good Night

Unknown

NOTE
2

Lowell Mason

Sing good night, good night, our part - ing lay, And

then we all to home will hie a - way, So join to

When *sol* is sharped in a song in the minor mode, we call the
scale structure the *harmonic minor*.

(26)

Dandelion

Paraphrased

NOTE

Italian Folk Song
from Abruzzi

Smoothly

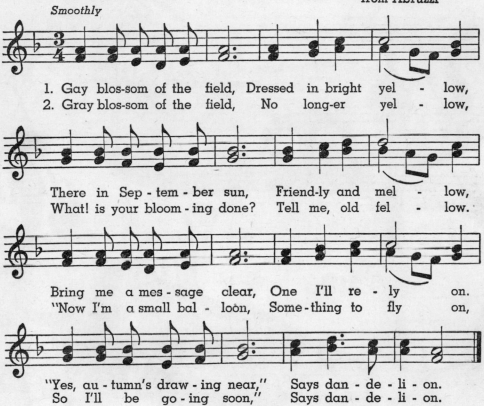

1. Gay blos-som of the field, Dressed in bright yel - low,
2. Gray blos-som of the field, No long-er yel - low,

There in Sep - tem - ber sun, Friend-ly and mel - low,
What! is your bloom - ing done? Tell me, old fel - low.

Bring me a mes - sage clear, One I'll re - ly on.
"Now I'm a small bal - loon, Some - thing to fly on,

"Yes, au - tumn's draw - ing near," Says dan - de - li - on.
So I'll be go - ing soon," Says dan - de - li - on.

Turn to page 234 for orchestra parts.

Italy was at one time the capital of the artistic world. During the fifteenth and sixteenth centuries such great artists as Botticelli, Leonardo da Vinci, and Michelangelo lived and worked there. In the little town of Cremona there were developed the finest stringed instruments the world has ever known. Even today these instruments are used by great violinists and cellists.

The Gondolier

Adapted ROTE Peruchino

In swinging rhythm

On the Grand Ca - nal we're boat - ing, In a

gon - do - la la - zi - ly float - ing, Thro' the shad - ows slow - ly

rid - ing, O - ver shim - mer - ing wa - ters we glide.

A - long the stream we si - lent - ly go as the

boat-man is stead - i - ly row - ing, With a sweep of the oar He

slowly   in time

fol - lows the shore. Ah, —————— love - ly Ven - ice,

we a - dore thee, With the soft sum - mer stars beam - ing

o'er thee, Touch-ing an-cient vil-las bright-ly

In the sil-ver-y gleam of the night.

Liszt used this melody in his composition for piano called "Naples and Venice."

The Homeless Man

Translated from
Frederick Holm

NOTE

Brahms

Moderately fast

mp.

No house and no fire-side, no wife and no child,

A-lone as a leaf in the cold win-ter wild;

Now up and now down-ward, now here and now there;

The world does not need me, so why should I care? —

Brahms wrote many songs as well as larger instrumental compositions. A musical composition is called an *opus*. This song is Opus 94, No. 5 in Brahms's works.

(30)

Salerno Fishermen

Adapted   NOTE   Italian Folk Song

Football

Russel Godfrey   ROTE   Charles Crane

In march time

1. There's a game that we play ev-'ry aft-er-noon in fall:
2. For a score near the goal you can hear the cap-tain call:

First a kick and then a catch and we're run-ning with the ball.
"Ev-'ry play-er in his place; get the sig-nal, one and all.

Let's be-gin! We can win! If we lose, we'll be cheer-ing just the same.
On your toes! There it goes!" It's a pass that will win the Ti-ger fame.

Chorus

mp

Down the field, thro' the line, o-ver tack-le, 'round the end All the

mp

Down the field, through the line,

way to the goal our op-po-nents must de-fend, Play by play;

f

O'er the goal, 'round the end, Play by play;

That's the way We will win a foot-ball game.

Try-ing ev-'ry way, We will win the game.

The New Highway

James Tippett   ROTE   J. Wolverton

Flowing, well accented

mf

Smooth-ly and eas-i-ly on we wont A-long the new

high-way of stone and ce-ment, We saw the farms and

fields of grass A - long the new high - way as

smooth as glass. Crowds of cit - y folk trav - eled fast, A -

long the new high - way they met and passed. Farm-ers, too, went

slower

up and down A - long the new high-way in - to the

in time

town. Mile up-on mile and day aft - er day,

f

Now we can ride on the new high - way.

(34)

The Airman's Song

Lucile Hildinger   NOTE   Grace V. Wilson

1. Our fa - thers cruised the o - cean, they sailed the earth a -
2. To - day, with earth - ways chart - ed on all the land and

round; Great con - ti - nents and is - lands with
sea, The trails a - long the air - ways are

peo - ple strange were found; Our fa - thers crossed the
o - pen wide for me; I'll soar a - bove the

prai - rie in cov - ered wag - on train, They
moun - tains and like a rock - et fly To

cleared the field and for - est and plant - ed fruit - ful grain.
find new paths of glo - ry in ev - 'ry dis - tant sky.

Pitch Names

The pitch names, or letter names, of the lines and spaces of the staff are as follows:

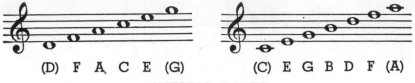

(D)   F   A   C   E   (G)   (C)   E   G   B   D   F   (A)

SPELLING GAMES

Many words can be spelled from the pitch names of the lines and spaces of the staff. For example:

C   A   B   E   G   G

1. Draw a staff on the blackboard and place some notes on it to spell a word. Ask someone to write the pitch names under the notes. If he spells the notes correctly, it is his turn to write another word with notes.

2. Spell a word under the staff with letters and ask someone to place the correct notes above the letters on the staff.

Keyboard Names

Here are the pitch names, or letter names, for the piano keyboard:

C D E F G A B C D E, etc.

KEYBOARD GAMES

Use a keyboard chart or draw a keyboard on the blackboard.

1. Spell a word, pointing to the keys.

2. Spell a word by playing the correct notes on a piano. Ask a friend to identify it. If he is right, it is his turn to spell.

The Crab

Translated freely   NOTE   Brazilian Folk Song

Steadily

1. When a crab is in the o - cean, With an un - du - lat - ing
2. Should he take a crab - by no - tion To go walk - ing by the

mo - tion, He is ver - y much at home with all the
o - cean, He ap - pears to be no fish at all while

crea - tures of the sea. Swish, swish, swish, he swish - es,
crawl - ing on the sand. Click, click, click, he's click - ing,

Down a - mong the fish - es. Oh, a crab is not a
With his side - wise kick - ing. Oh, a crab is not a

fish and yet a fish he seems to be.
fish be - cause no fish can swim on land.

Brazilian boys and girls play an amusing game with this song.
When they come to "Swish, swish, swish" and "Click, click, click,"
they make sounds with their hands in imitation of the crab.

Americas, Shake Hands

Reid A. Cameron   ROTE   Mercedes Navarro Cameron

Moderately

1. Co-lum-bus start-ed some-thing by sail-ing o-ver here;
2. By toil-ing, bleed-ing, think-ing, each fa-ther and each son

Oth - ers fol - lowed   lat - er   to   this   West - ern Hem - i - sphere,
Built   the   might - y   na-tions and re - pub - lics twen - ty - one;

Peo - ple   of   all   na - tions,   peo - ple   of   all   creeds
If   out - side   our   bor - ders   tyr - an - nies ap - pear,

Com - ing here   for   free-dom   and   for   glo-rious deeds!
Join   our   hands   in   un - ion,   voic-ing   love   and   cheer!

A-mer-i-cas, shake hands! — North, Cen-tral, and South —

A-mer-i-cas, sing out   our lib-er-ty, so dear to you and me!

Form a un-ion   none can sev-er;   Let us   live

and love for-ev-er,   Liv-ing, work-ing   all to-geth-er,

Not "Ma-ña-na"—now or nev-er!   A-mer-i-cas,

shake hands! — North, Cen-tral, and South   A-mer-i-cas,

"A-mi-gos" all,   "U-ni-dos" all,   shake hands!

The Parrot

Translated   ROTE   Venezuelan Game Song

Gaily

1. When a par-rot to the church   goes,   He is read-y, Mad-am
2. When a par-rot pays at-ten   -   tion   To a la - dy we could
3. When two par-rots live to - geth   -   er,   Din-ing is for them a

1. When a par-rot to the church   goes,
2. When a par-rot pays at - ten   -   tion
3. When two par-rots live to-geth   -   er,

Poll   knows, For she wash-es ev -'ry Mon   -   day
men   -   tion, Poll - y sheds her feath-ers old   -   en
pleas   -   ure; With-out knife or fork they're skill   -   ful,

He is read - y, Mad-am Poll   knows,   For she wash - es ev -'ry
To a la - dy we could men   -   tion,   Poll-y sheds her feath-ers
Din-ing is for them a pleas   -   ure;   With-out knife or fork they're

Chorus

All his trou - sers just for Sun - day.   Hi there,   my
For some new ones green and gold - en.
All they do is take a bill full.

Mon   -   day,   Sun - day.   Qua, qua!
old   -   en,   gold - en.
skill   -   ful,   bill full.

In the Early Morning

Translated   NOTE   Brazilian Folk Song

When I asked her for a blos-som, she would on-ly tell me   no;
All the friends I called to help me could not break a sin-gle strand

When I asked a - gain, she cut a cord and bound it to   me   so.
Of the cord se - cure-ly fas-tened by the an-gel's gra-cious hand.

The Meat-Pie Seller

Translated   NOTE   Chilean Street Cry

Moderately

From the   ov - en, hot and   tast - y,   Of
A   las de hor - no co - mo   fue - go,   Con

beef, rai - sins, eggs, and on - ions.   Em - pa - na - das, em - pa-
pa - sa a - cei - tu - na y   hue - vo.   Em - pa - na - das do - min-

na - das! Come and   buy   for your Sun-day break - fast.
gue - ras,   pa - ra   la   gen ——— te chi - le - na.

Humberto Allende, a Chilean composer, used this street song in
his tone poem "La voz de las calles" (The Voice of the Streets).

The Ship from Heaven

Translated · NOTE · Brazilian Game Song
Arr. by H. Villa-Lobos

Ah, come walk a-long the o-cean, The gold-en beach-es by; —
See her se-rene-ly glid-ing, As an-gels swing the oars,—

We shall see a ship ap-proach-ing Which has fall-en from the sky!
Row a-long the flow'r-strewn wa-ter, Bring your car-go to our shores.

We shall see a ship ap-proach-ing Which has fall-en from the sky!
Row a-long the flow'r-strewn wa-ter, Bring your car-go to our shores.

The natural sign (♮) before *ti* makes the note *te* (tay).

SYNCOPATION

Much of the music of certain peoples has complicated and complex rhythm patterns which are too difficult for the average person to play and sing. Our modern composers are using more and more of these rhythms. What makes this music interesting? It is syncopation, which is produced by giving a note an accent when none is expected. In the pattern below, the last part of the first beat is accented and carried over into the first part of the second beat.

Standard beat: 4/4

Syncopation: 4/4

Beat

Ring the Banjo

Stephen Foster

ROTE

Stephen Foster

Brightly and fast

syncopation

1. The time is nev-er drear-y If a fel-low nev-er
— come a-gain, Su-san-na, By the gas-light of the

2. Oh, nev-er count the bub-bles While there's wa-ter in the
— beau-ties of cre-a-tion Will nev-er lose their

groans, A par-ty's nev-er wea-ry
moon, We'll tum the old pi-an-o
spring, A man can have no trou-bles
charm, While I roam the old plan-ta-tion

Solo instrument or dancer

1. **2.**

With the rat-tle of the bones. Then
When the ban-jo's out of tune.
While he's got this song to sing. The
With my true love on my arm.

Chorus

Ring, ring the ban-jo! I like that good old song.

Come a-gain, my true love, Oh, where you been so long?

(44)

Play "Ring the Banjo" on the bongo and bones. A bongo consists of a pair of drums of slightly different size lashed together. The player clamps the drums between his knees and plays on both surfaces. Bones consist of a pair of six-inch sticks held in each hand.

Play the instruments throughout the song. One solo instrument or a dancer, or both, may improvise an accompaniment on the last phrase of the verse.

THE GIRL I LEFT BEHIND ME

This melody, sometimes called "Brighton Camp," goes back to the eighteenth century. It is associated with the British Army, for it is often played when British troops leave for service abroad. A small group may whistle the tune while the rest of the class sings "Ring the Banjo."

Stephen Foster was greatly influenced by the music of the Negroes. No people have brought to our shores a richer contribution to rhythm and harmony than have our people of African descent. Dvořák, the Bohemian composer (1841-1904), heard their music when he visited America and used some of the harmonies and rhythms in his "New World Symphony." Such rhythms and harmonies are being used by many of our American composers of today.

Gentle Annie

Stephen Foster   NOTE   Stephen Foster

1. Thou wilt come no more, gen-tle An-nie,
2. We have roamed and loved 'mid the bow-ers,

Like a flow'r thy spir-it did de-part;
When thy down-y cheeks were in their bloom;

Thou art gone, a-las, like the man-y
Now I stand a-lone by the flow-ers

That have bloomed in the sum-mer of my heart.
While they min-gle their per-fume o'er thy tomb.

Shall we nev-er more be-hold thee, Nev-er

hear thy win-ning voice a-gain, When the spring-time comes, gen-tle

An-nie, — When the wild flow'rs are scat-tered o'er the plain?

Down in the Valley

Traditional ROTE Kentucky Mountain Ballad

Smoothly

1. Down in the val-ley, the val-ley so low, —
2. Ros-es love sun-shine, — ros-es love dew, —
3. Build me a cas-tle — for-ty feet high, —

Hang your head o-ver, hear the wind blow; —
An-gels in heav-en know I love you; —
So I can see you as you go by; —

Hear the wind blow, dear, hear the wind blow, —
Know I love you, dear, know I love you, —
As you go by, dear, as you go by, —

Hang your head o-ver, hear the wind blow. —
An-gels in heav-en know I love you. —
So I can see you as you go by. —

Ellen Bayne

Stephen Foster   NOTE   Stephen Foster

1. Soft be thy slum - bers,   rude cares de - part,
2. Dream not in an - guish,   dream not in fear,
3. Scenes that have van - ished   smile on thee now,

Vi - sions in num - bers   cheer thy young heart;
Love shall not lan - guish,   fond ones are near;
Pleas - ures once ban - ished   play 'round thy brow;

Dream on, while bright hours and   fond hopes re - main,
Sleep - ing or wak - ing, in   pleas - ure or pain,
Forms long de - part - ed —   greet thee a - gain,

Bloom - ing like smil - ing bow'rs for thee, El - len Bayne.
Warm hearts will beat for thee, — Sweet El - len Bayne.
Sooth - ing thy dream - ing heart, — Sweet El - len Bayne.

Chorus

Gen - tle slum - bers o'er thee glide, dreams of beau - ty 'round thee bide,

(48)

While I lin-ger by thy side, Sweet El - len Bayne.

Wayfaring Stranger

Traditional   ROTE   Spiritual

Moderately slow

I'm just a poor way-far-ing stran-ger A-trav'ling

thro' this world of woe, But there's no sick - ness, toil nor dan-ger

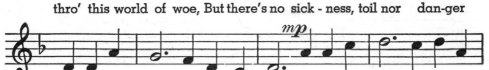

In that bright world to which I go; I'm go-ing there to see my

fa - ther, I'm go-ing there no more to roam, I'm just a-
(mother)
(brother)

slower

go - ing o - ver Jor-dan, I'm just a- go - ing o-ver home.

(49)

Drivin' Steel

Traditional   NOTE   American Work Song

Moderately with steady swing

1. Driv - in' steel, (Huh) Driv - in' steel, (Huh)
2. Treat me right, (Huh) Treat me right, (Huh)

Driv - in' steel, boys, is hard work, I know;
Treat me right, boys, I'm bound to stay all day;

Driv - in' steel, (Huh) Driv - in' steel, (Huh)
Treat me wrong, (Huh) Treat me wrong, (Huh)

Driv - in' steel, boys, is hard work, I know.
Treat me wrong, boys, I'm bound to run a - way.

Work songs are used as a rhythm accompaniment to manual labor. Just as sailors on the old sailing vessels used chanteys to lighten their tasks, so men working with hammers, picks, and axes use grunts and the sounds of tools in rhythmic answer to a melody carried by the leader. These work songs are gradually disappearing, as modern machines have largely replaced man power. One of the most famous work songs in the world is "Song of the Volga Boatmen," sung by Russian workmen as they pulled the towlines of boats along the Volga River. Perhaps you can listen to a recording of it.

You might try to compose a work song of your own.

(50)

The Shepherd Boy

Translated   ROTE   Greek Mountain Song

Mournfully

1. Moun - tain shep-herd, sad and lone - ly,
2. Na - ture now is gray and som - ber,

O - ver rock-y pas-tures wea-ri-ly I go,
Streams of melt-ed snow no long-er swift-ly sing,

Dream - ing here of home so dis - tant,
Flow'rs are fad - ing thro' the val - ley,

Friend and neigh-bor in my vil-lage down be - low.
Birds of sum-mer for a warm-er land take wing.

Refrain

All my sor - row, all my long-ing Soft - ly on my shep-herd's

flute of reed I play; Breez - es waft my

mourn-ful pip-ing, Bear the ech - o far a - way.

(51)

Barb'ry Allen

Traditional

NOTE

Old Ballad sung in the
Appalachian Highlands

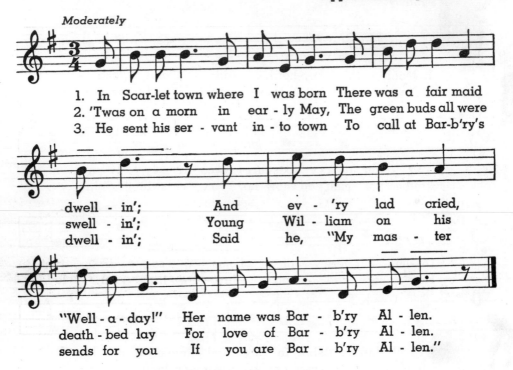

Moderately

1. In Scar-let town where I was born There was a fair maid
2. 'Twas on a morn in ear - ly May, The green buds all were
3. He sent his ser - vant in - to town To call at Bar-b'ry's

dwell - in';   And   ev - 'ry   lad   cried,
swell - in';   Young Wil - liam on   his
dwell - in';   Said   he, "My   mas - ter

"Well - a - day!" Her   name was Bar - b'ry Al - len.
death - bed lay   For   love of Bar - b'ry Al - len.
sends for you   If   you are Bar - b'ry Al - len."

4. Then slowly, slowly up she rose
   And slowly she came nigh him
   And said as by his form she stood,
   "My lad, I think you're dyin'."

5. He turned his face unto the wall,
   For death was in him dwellin',
   And said, "No better can I be
   Till I wed Barb'ry Allen."

6. When he was gone and in his grave,
   Her heart was sick with sorrow;
   She cried, "Oh, Mother, make my bed,
   For I will die tomorrow."

7. They placed her in the old churchyard,
   Young William's grave was nigh her;
   And from his mound a red rose grew,
   From hers a cruel briar.

8. The vines grew up the churchyard wall,
   Till they could climb no higher,
   All wrapped and turned in lovers' knots,
   The rose around the briar.

The Weary Traveler

Traditional   NOTE   Spiritual

1. Let us cheer the wea-ry trav-el-er a-long,
2. There's a star a-bove that's beck-on-ing to me,
3. I can hear the trum-pets ech-o-ing a-round,

Cheer the wea-ry trav-el-er; Let us cheer the wea-ry
Star a-bove that's beck-on-ing; There's a star a-bove that's
Hear the trum-pets ech-o-ing; I can hear the trum-pets

trav-el-er A - long the heav-en-ly way.
beck-on-ing A - long the heav-en-ly way.
ech-o-ing A - long the heav-en-ly way.

Roundup Lullaby

Badger Clark   ROTE   Cowboy Song

Lazily
Melody in the second part

1. Des - ert sil - ver blue be - neath the pale star - shine,
2. Noth - in' there a - long the plains that you folks need,

Coy - ote yap - pin' la - zy on the hill.
Noth - in' there that seems to take your eye.

Sleep - y winks of light a - long the far sky - line,
Still ya' got to watch 'em or they'll all stam - pede,

Time for mill - in' cat - tle to be still. —
Plung - in' down an ar - roy - o to die. —

So now, the light - ning's far a - way, The

lone-some owl is call - in', The night is soft - ly fall - in',

(54)

So now, there'll come an-oth-er day. Oh,

Set-tle down, you cat-tle, till the morn - ing.

Oh, Worship the King

Sir Robert Grant   NOTE   Haydn

Firmly

mf

1. Oh, wor-ship the King, All - glo-rious a - bove!
2. Thy boun-ti-ful care what tongue can re - cite?

Oh, grate-ful-ly sing His pow-er and His love!
It breathes in the air, it shines in the light,

mp   *mf*

Our shield and de-fend-er, the An-cient of Days,
It streams from the hills, it de-scends to the plain

Pa - vil-ioned in splen-dor and gird - ed with praise.
And sweet-ly dis-tills in the dew and the rain.

The Tall Pine Tree

G. F. McKay   NOTE   G. F. McKay

Joyfully rhythmic

1. Oh, the tall pine tree, so strong and free,
2. Oh, the pine is long and gaunt and strong

With branch-es thrust-ing high, From the moun-tain-side up-
As it reach-es for the sun; With its friend - ly arms out-

grow-ing With shoul-ders in the sky; O- ver cliff and crag,
spread-ing It wel-comes ev-'ry-one; O-ver flocks and herds,

O - ver stream and lake, O - ver all the wood-land scene
O - ver nest - ing birds, O - ver you and o - ver me

The might-y pine tree tow-ers, Ward-er of the for-est green.
The tall pine tree is stand-ing In ver-dant maj-es - ty.

Musical Friends

In 1809, the year made notable by the birth of our own Abraham Lincoln, two men destined to be numbered among the great in music were born in Europe — Felix Mendelssohn in Germany and Frédéric Chopin in Poland. Robert Schumann was born a year later in Germany, and Franz Liszt two years later in Hungary. These four men so closely linked by time were also associated by the nature of their work as musicians. All were famous as pianists and composers, although Schumann devoted himself chiefly to writing, leaving the interpretive side of music to his gifted wife, Clara.

Mendelssohn, Chopin, Schumann, and Liszt had frequent occasions to perform and hear each other's works, and all lived on friendly terms throughout their lives.

Mendelssohn was a prodigy as performer, composer, and conductor. He wrote his "Midsummer-Night's Dream" overture when he was only seventeen. That remains one of his best-known works, although he wrote in all forms. His two great oratorios, "St. Paul" and "Elijah," are often heard today.

Chopin has been called "the poet of the piano." He was both a sensitive performer and a gifted composer. The titles he most frequently employed for his compositions are ballade, étude, prelude, nocturne, and fantasia, although he also used such dance forms as the mazurka, polonaise, and waltz.

Schumann wrote many works for the piano, some great songs, four symphonies, and instrumental compositions for small groups. He was an outstanding critic and writer about music.

Liszt was one of the greatest pianists who ever lived. He perfected a form called the "symphonic poem." He used Hungarian folk themes in many of his compositions and made piano transcriptions of the works of Bach, Schubert, Beethoven, Wagner, and others.

On Wings of Song

Translated from
Heinrich Heine

ROTE

Mendelssohn

Slowly and tranquilly

1. On wings of gold - en mu - sic,
vio - lets shy - ly twin - kle,

Be - lov - ed, we will fly Far o'er the Gan - ges
They smile at stars a - bove; Ros - es are whis - p'ring

Riv - er Where beau - ti - ful mead - ows lie; And
soft - ly Their mys - ti - cal tales of love; All

there in a red-blos-somed gar - den In qui - et moon - light
grace-ful-ly leap-ing and play-ing Go swift and tim-id ga-

gradually louder

glow — The lo - tus blooms are wait - ing Their
zelles, — While thro' the dis - tant val - ley The

softer

sis - ter fair to know, — The lo - tus blooms are
rum - bling cur - rent swells, — While thro' the dis - tant

wait - ing Their sis - ter fair to know. 2. The
val - ley The rum-bling cur-rent swells.

So there we shall be to - geth - er

gradually louder

un - der the shad - y palm And share our love for-

softer

ev - er Mid dreams of bliss-ful calm, — Mid dreams of

bliss - ful calm, Dreams — of calm. —

Play this melody on your violins and flutes.

Lovely Messengers

Adapted from
the Bible

ROTE

Mendelssohn

Slowly with motion

How love-ly are the mes-sen-gers that preach us the gos-pel of peace,

How love-ly are the mes-sen-gers that preach us the gos-pel of peace,

The gos - pel of peace, — The mes-sen-gers that

How love - ly are the mes - sen - gers that

preach — us the gos - pel of peace,

preach us the gos - pel of peace, How love - ly are the

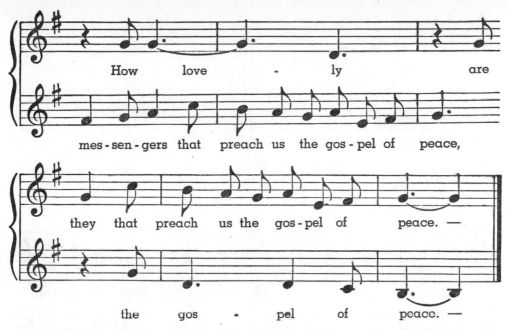

How love - ly are
mes-sen-gers that preach us the gos-pel of peace,
they that preach us the gos-pel of peace. —
the gos - pel of peace. —

This song is from the oratorio "St. Paul." It sounds well when it is played as a violin duet.

Good Morning

Björnson ROTE Grieg

High in the heav - ens ris - es the sun, Glow - ing with fire as
day is be - gun, O - ver the moun-tain - top break - ing,
Slum-ber-ing na-ture a - wak - ing. Rise, a-rise, the birds all sing!

Rise, a-rise, a wel-come bring! Greet-ing the ear-ly morn-ing,

mf

Greet-ing the ear-ly morn-ing, Wake, a-rise, a-

f

rise, a-rise! The birds all sing. Wake, a-rise, a-

pp

rise, a-rise! A wel-come bring. Hear the birds sing!

mf

Wel-come they bring. Hear the birds sing!

f

Wel-come they bring, Greet-ing the ear-ly morn-ing.

Edvard Grieg (1843-1907) was a great Norwegian composer. In his youth he was aided and encouraged by Franz Liszt, who helped bring recognition of his talents. Many of Grieg's songs and dances reflect the beauty and spirit of his native land, which he loved dearly and in which he spent the greater part of his life. His best-known compositions are the two suites called "Peer Gynt" and the Concerto in A Minor for the piano.

Björnstjerne Björnson (1832-1910) was one of Norway's greatest writers. In 1903 he received the Nobel prize in literature.

To the Moon

Adapted from
Karl Enslin

NOTE

Bavarian Folk Song

La - dy Moon, a - bove me glid - ing,
Like a queen se - rene - ly rid - ing,

With your clear re - flect - ed light,
Thro' the pur - ple shades of

night, of night; In your beau - ty, in your splen - dor, Peace - ful

calm and still - ness lie, — Send - ing

down a mes - sage ten - der

From your throne a - bove the sky.

Anna Maria

Translated

NOTE

Dutch Folk Song

Brightly

1. "Well, An - na Ma - ri - a, oh, where do you go?
Boys:
2. "Well, An - na Ma - ri - a, what will you do then?
3. "Well, An - na Ma - ri - a, of sol - diers be - ware;

You need a com-pan-ion, now do not say no!"
There's no place for wom - en a - mong sol - dier men."
I seek a nice maid - en, my for - tune to share."

" I. go a - walk - ing, with sol - dier men talk - ing,
Girls: "Wash - ing and spin - ning, some sol - dier man win - ning,
"That I'm not need - ing, be done with your plead - ing,

Fa la la, fa la la," said An - na Ma - rie.

In $\frac{6}{8}$ meter, there are three rhythms:

running

skipping

walking

Beat

Clap and step the rhythm of each pattern several times. Which pattern is found in the song above?

The Sweepers of Calais

Paraphrased NOTE Breton Game Song

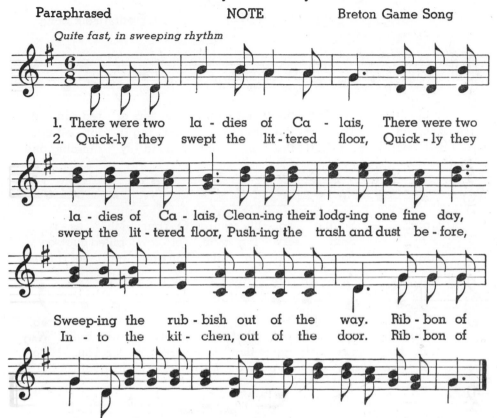

Quite fast, in sweeping rhythm

1. There were two la - dies of Ca - lais, There were two
2. Quick-ly they swept the lit - tered floor, Quick - ly they

la - dies of Ca - lais, Clean-ing their lodg-ing one fine day,
swept the lit - tered floor, Push-ing the trash and dust be - fore,

Sweep-ing the rub - bish out of the way. Rib - bon of
In - to the kit - chen, out of the door. Rib - bon of

yel - low, rib-bon of crim-son, Wear a col - ored rib - bon to - day.
yel - low, rib-bon of crim-son, Wear a col - ored rib - bon to - day.

3. Out of the doorway, through the yard,
Out of the doorway, through the yard,
Working along with disregard,
Fin'lly they reached the gay boulevard.

4. Out of the town they swept away,
Out of the town they swept away,
Far from the borders of Calais.
Where did they go? Nobody can say.

This song has a combination of all three rhythms: running, walking, and skipping.

Good Dagobert

Translated NOTE **French Folk Song**

Fast

1. Good Dag - o - bert, the King, wore trou - sers of red in - side
2. Good Dag - o - bert, the King, went hunt - ing in for - est near
3. Good Dag - o - bert, the King, was rap - id - ly run - ning one

out. — Said a no - ble squire, "O Your Maj - es - ty,
by. — Said a serv - ing man, "Yel - low - billed cuck-oo
day. — Said a roy - al duke, "You are out of breath;

You are in - side out; that can nev - er be!" "Why
Is the kind of game that is best for you." "Be
If you run so hard, you will choke to death." "O

not, sir?" said the King. "I'm roy - al in an - y old thing!" —
still," His High-ness said. "I'll aim at the top of your head." —
my," the King be - wailed, "A rab - bit was scent-ing the trail." —

4. Good Dagobert, the King,
   Was out for a voyage by sea.
   Said a sailor man, "If the ship goes down,
   Why, Your Majesty will most surely drown."
   "Quite true, but some may think
   I needed the water to drink."

What rhythm patterns are found in this song?

The Fiddler

Translated   NOTE   Norwegian Folk Song

Gaily

1. There once was a fid - dler with on - ly one cow;
2. He res - ined his bow and he tuned ev - 'ry string,
3. "If I grow as old as the moss on the tree,"

To get him some mu - sic, he did not care how;
He scraped on the fid - dle, and how it did sing!
The fid - dler ex-claimed, "I shall nev - er a - gree

He trad - ed the cow for a fid - dle, and then
As boys and their maid - ens went danc - ing a - round,
To bar - ter my fid - dle for cat - tle or sheep,

With mu - sic at hand he was hap - py a - gain.
The coun - try - side ech - oed the rol - lick - ing sound.
For mu - sic is bet - ter than crit - ters to keep."

"Old vi - o-lin, go fid-dle um dum, fid-dle um dum dum dum do."

Nicolas and Marie

Paraphrased

ROTE

French Song
Seventeenth Century

Not too fast

1. Young Nic - o - las went call — ing, on pret - ty Jeanne Ma - rie. Said he, "When leaves are fall — ing, Oh, will you mar - ry me?"
2. Sad Nic - o - las went cry — ing, "O cru - el Jeanne Ma - rie! The fall - en leaves are ly — ing a - round us, as you see."

1. Young Nic - o - las went call - ing on Miss Jeanne Ma - rie. Said he, "When leaves are fall - ing, will you mar - ry me?"
2. Sad Nic - o - las went cry - ing, "Cru - el Jeanne Ma - rie! The fall - en leaves are ly - ing round us, as you see."

She shook her head in scorn, —
Just then on wild wind borne, —

She shook in scorn,
On wild wind borne,

"Like - ly that will nev - er be, For I shall
Whirl - ing, twirl - ing mer - ri - ly, The danc - ing,

"Like - ly that will nev - er be, I'll
Whirl - ing, twirl - ing mer - ri - ly, The

wed when-e'er the leaves Up - ward fall from ground to tree."
gold - en au - tumn leaves Up - ward swept from ground to tree.

wed when-e'er the leaves Fall up - ward to the tree."
gold-en au-tumn leaves Swept up-ward to the tree.

(69)

The Legend of St. Nicolas

Translated NOTE **French Song**
Sixteenth Century

Moderately fast

Three chil-dren wan-dered o'er the plain, three lit - tle

Sing this refrain before the first and after the final stanza.

End

chil-dren glean-ing grain. 1. A butch-er's cot-tage came in
2. When scarce-ly past the en - trance
3. Now aft - er sev - en wea - ry

sight. "O butch-er, may we stay the night?" "Come in, come
hall, The wick - ed butch - er killed them all; He chopped them
years The good Saint Nic - o - las ap - pears. Be - fore the

in, my chil - dren three! Quite sure - ly you may lodge with me."
up in piec - es fine And threw them in a tub of brine.
butch-er's door he cried, "O butch - er, may I come in - side?"

4. "Come in, come in, St. Nicolas!
 'Twould be a sin to let you pass."
 No sooner in the house he stood
 Than Nicolas demanded food.

5. "Perhaps you'd like a bit of ham."
 "No, thank you, hungry as I am."
 "Then maybe veal you would prefer."
 "Nor any veal for me, good sir."

6. "Some meat well salted down with brine
 For seven years would suit me fine,"
 The butcher heard with sad dismay;
 Outside the door, he ran away.

7. "O butcher, butcher, do not flee!
 Repent, and God will pardon thee."
 St. Nicolas does not despair
 At these three children lying there.

8. "O little children, bless your fate,
 For I'm St. Nicolas, the Great."
 He pointed fingers, one, two, three;
 The children rose for all to see.

9. The first one cried, "My sleep is through!"
 The second yawned and said, "Me, too."
 The third exclaimed in great surprise,
 "I think this must be Paradise!"

The Orphan Girl

Translated   NOTE   Latvian Folk Song

Slowly and sadly

1. All a-lone in grief I wan-der On the mead-ow with my sheep,

By the mounds in or-chard yon-der Where be-lov-ed par-ents sleep.

2. Friends no longer stand beside me,
 Days are long and nights are cold;
 Warmth and care alike denied me,
 Neighbor children nag and scold.

3. Fondly to my mother calling,
 Sad I roam 'neath leaden skies;
 Like the orchard blossoms falling,
 Tears are dropping from my eyes.

The Slumbering Cathedral

J. W. Beattie   ROTE   Charles Widor

Be-neath the star - ry dome of the skies,
Her jew-eled win - dows dark-ened from sight,

Hm

With tow - ers bathed in ce - les - tial light,
The great ca - the - dral in slum - ber lies.

Hm

The great ca - the - dral slum - ber - ing lies,

Hm

Charles Widor (1845-1937) spent his long musical life as organist of the Church of St. Sulpice in Paris. For more than fifty years he was famous as organist and composer. This melody is from his Fourth Symphony. Felix Guilmant and César Franck were other great Parisian organists and composers who lived at about the same time.

You will find syncopation in the fifth and sixth phrases.

Ca-ressed by winds of the sum - mer night.

Hm — — — — — —

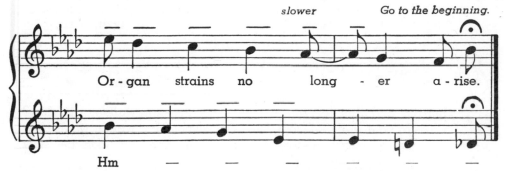

With - in is si - lence, thro' the nave

Hm — — — — —

slower　　　*Go to the beginning.*

Or - gan strains no long - er a - rise.

Hm — — — — —

The Boat Maiden

Paraphrased   NOTE   **French Dialogue Song**

Not too fast

1. "Where do you go, fair maid - en? An - swer me now, pray
2. "Where do you live, fair maid - en? An - swer me now, pray
3. "Why be so stub - born, maid - en? An - swer me now, pray

tell." — "I go to Plou - gas - tel, sir,
tell." — "There in that riv - er boat, sir,
tell." — "I want af - fec - tion on - ly,

Ber-ries and fruit to sell." —"Do you not know walk-ing is slow?
Close by your wall and moat." —"Do you not know win-ter winds blow
Sad is my life a - lone." —"Do you not know I can be - stow

Why not go rid - ing with me? I pass this way
I - ci - ly cold from the sea? Come and be warm
Love and af - fec - tion so free? You have my heart,

'most ev - 'ry day. Jump in my car-riage and see."
out of the storm, Snug in my cas - tle with me."
why live a - part? Come and be hap - py with me."

"No, no! I an-swer no! Walk-ing a-lone I go.
"No, no! I an-swer no! Liv-ing a-lone I go.
"Yes, yes! I an-swer yes! I'll buy a wed-ding dress.

Your man-ner is pret-ty, your lan-guage is wit-ty,
Your man-ner is pret-ty, your lan-guage is wit-ty,
Your man-ner is pret-ty, your lan-guage is wit-ty,

I like your horse and car-riage too. But tho' you are charm-ing,
I like your wall and cas-tle too. But tho' you are charm-ing,
I like your face and for-tune too. I find you are charm-ing,

I find you a-larm-ing. I can-not go rid-ing with you."
I find you a-larm-ing. I can-not be liv-ing with you."
No long-er a-larm-ing. I'll mar-ry and tar-ry with you."

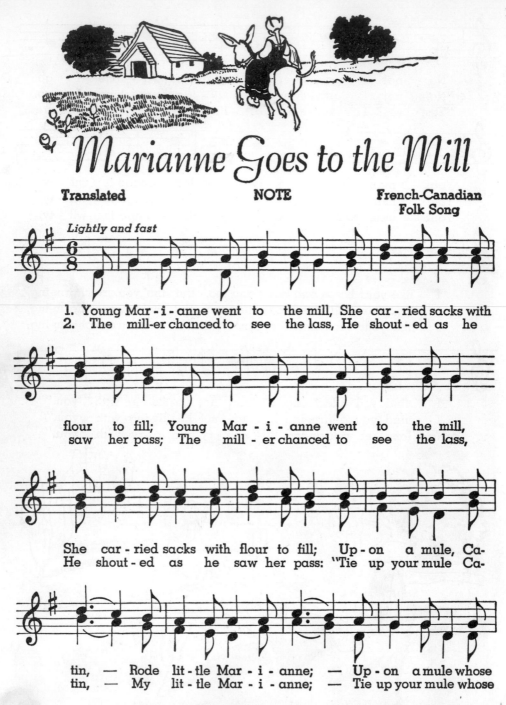

Marianne Goes to the Mill

Translated   NOTE   French-Canadian
Folk Song

Lightly and fast

1. Young Mar - i - anne went to the mill, She car - ried sacks with
2. The mill-er chanced to see the lass, He shout - ed as he

flour to fill; Young Mar - i - anne went to the mill,
saw her pass; The mill - er chanced to see the lass,

She car - ried sacks with flour to fill; Up - on a mule, Ca-
He shout - ed as he saw her pass: "Tie up your mule Ca-

tin, — Rode lit - tle Mar - i - anne; — Up - on a mule whose
tin, — My lit - tle Mar - i - anne; — Tie up your mule whose

name was Ca - tin   She jour - neyed   to   the mill.
name is   Ca - tin   Way out be - hind   the mill."

3. Now as the mill went round and round,
    A wolf came prowling, mischief bound;
    Now as the mill went round and round,
    A wolf came prowling, mischief bound;
    He ate the mule Catin of little Marianne;
    He ate the mule whose name was Catin,
    Tied there behind the mill.

4. Then Marianne began to cry,
    The miller gave her gold to buy,
    Then Marianne began to cry,
    The miller gave her gold to buy
    Another mule Catin for little Marianne;
    Another mule whose name was Catin;
    She trotted from the mill.

5. But as the mule the father spied,
    He shook his head and madly cried;
    But as the mule the father spied,
    He shook his head and madly cried:
    "Oh, where is old Catin, my little Marianne?
    Oh, where's the mule whose name is Catin,
    Who journeyed to the mill?"

6. "Today is good St. Michael's Day,
    When mules all turn from brown to gray;
    Today is good St. Michael's Day,
    When mules all turn from brown to gray;
    This is the same Catin," said little Marianne,
    "This is the mule whose name is Catin,
    Who took me to the mill."

Catin is pronounced to rhyme with Marianne.

In My Bark Canoe

Translated   NOTE   French-Canadian
Voyageur Song

Smoothly

1. Float - ing free in my birch ca-noe,   Un-der-neath the
2. Sides of bark has my birch ca-noe,   Sewn with twist-ed

clear o - pen sky, I brave all dan - ger and the
roots wo - ven fine; She rides the rap - ids, pass - ing

tem - pest too, Green hills pass - ing by; I brave all
safe - ly thro', Pad - dles clear white pine; She rides the

dan-ger and the tem-pest too, Green hills pass - ing by.
rap-ids, pass-ing safe - ly thro,' Pad-dles clear white pine.

3. When a portage I have to make,
   Naught but forest trees in my sight,
   My birch canoe upon my back, I take
   Shelter for the night;
   My birch canoe upon my back, I take
   Shelter for the night.

4. Farmers like their bright plows of steel,
   Hunters like their guns straight and true,
   The weaver likes a loom and spinning wheel;
   I, my bark canoe;
   The weaver likes a loom and spinning wheel;
   I, my bark canoe.

(79)

The Lass Canadian

Translated   NOTE   French-Canadian
Party Song

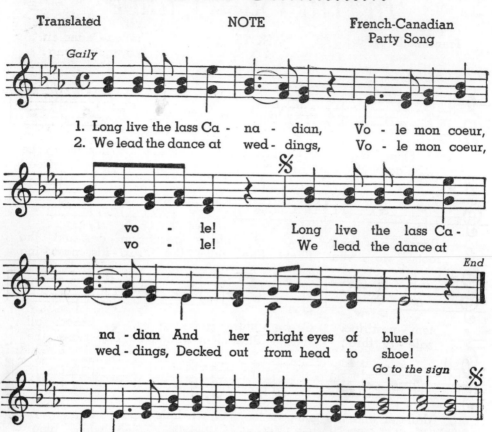

1. Long live the lass Ca - na - dian, Vo - le mon coeur,
2. We lead the dance at wed - dings, Vo - le mon coeur,

vo - le! Long live the lass Ca -
vo - le! We lead the dance at

na - dian And her bright eyes of blue!
wed - dings, Decked out from head to shoe!

And her bright eyes of blue, blue, blue, And her bright eyes, blue, blue.
Decked out from head to shoe, shoe, shoe, Decked out from head to shoe.

3. We make a party full of cheer, Vole mon coeur, vole!
   We make a party full of cheer, Good style in all we do!
   Good style in all we do, do, do, Good style in all we do.
   We make a party full of cheer, Good style in all we do.

4. So all the evening passes by, Vole mon coeur, vole!
   So all the evening passes by In friendship good and true!
   In friendship good and true, true, true, In friendship good and true.
   So all the evening passes by In friendship good and true.

The sign C means "common time," or $\frac{4}{4}$.

Evening Song

Arne Oldberg   ROTE   Austrian Folk Melody
Arr. by Arne Oldberg

Softly

Slow - ly gath-er the shad - ows o'er the val-leys and hills, — And gen-tly smiles the moon-light o'er the mead-ows and rills; — Soon dark-ness will en-fold us with the rest that our la-bors have won, — And peace-ful slum-ber hold us till the rise of the glo-ri-ous sun. —

Music of the British Isles

The people of the British Isles have made a great contribution to the musical life of the world, for the English, Irish, Scots, and Welsh have been among the chief settlers and colonizers of many lands. Wherever they have gone, they have established anew their songs, games, and dances.

In early colonial days the English brought into the highlands of our Appalachian region the ballads which are still sung there, much as they were in the time of Queen Elizabeth. Welsh miners who came to Pennsylvania and Ohio brought with them their majestic hymns and their love of singing. The Scots had their own rhythms and melodies which they carried along wherever they settled. The Irish added many a jig and melodic song to the gaiety of life in places far removed from the "old sod."

So "Loch Lomond," "Killarney," "Wraggle Taggle Gypsies," and hundreds of other songs are as likely to be known and loved in Canada, Australia, New Zealand, South Africa, the United States, and remote islands as in the land of their origin. Tune and text may have become altered in the process of travel but the story and melody have continued to bring pleasure and comfort to people in the far corners of the earth.

John Peel

John Graves NOTE North English Melody

Lively
Slowly and sadly on third stanza

1. D'ye ken John Peel with his coat so gay?
2. Yes, I ken John Peel and Ru - by, too,
3. D'ye ken John Peel with his coat so gay?

D'ye ken John Peel at the break o' the day?
And Ran - ger and Ring - wood, Bell - man and True;
He lived at Trout - beck once on a day,

D'ye ken John Peel when he's far, far a - way
From a find to a check, from a check to a view,
But now he has gone far a - way, far a - way;

With his hound and his horn in the morn - ing?
From a view to a death in the morn - ing.
We shall ne'er hear his voice in the morn - ing.

Refrain

For the sound of his horn brought me from my bed,

And the cry of the hounds which he oft - times led;

Peel's "View, hal - loo!" would a - wak - en the dead

Or the fox from his lair in the morn - ing.

Find = when the hounds pick up the scent
Check = when the hounds pause
View = when the hounds pursue the quarry

Loch Lomond

Unknown   ROTE   Scottish Folk Song

mf *Briskly*

1. By yon bon - nie banks and by yon bon - nie braes,
2. 'Twas there that we part - ed in yon shad - y glen

Where the sun shines bright on Loch Lo - mond,
On the steep, steep side of Ben Lo - mond,

Where me and my true love were ev - er wont to gae
Where in pur - ple hue the High-land hills we view

On the bon-nie, bon-nie banks of Loch Lo - mond.
And the moon com-ing out in the gloam - ing.

(84)

Oh, ye'll take the high road and I'll take the low road,

Melody

And I'll be in Scot - land a - fore ye, But

me and my true love we'll nev - er meet a - gain

On the bon-nie, bon - nie banks of Loch Lo - mond.

There are many interesting stories connected with this song. One is that it was first sung to his companion in arms by a Scottish soldier who lay fatally wounded on a battlefield in France. The "low road" is the path he felt his dying spirit would take to his homeland. The "high road" is the route of the living.

The Keel Row

Traditional   ROTE   Scottish Folk Song
Arr. by F. B. Cookson

Briskly

1. Sand - gate, Sand-gate, Sand-gate, Sand - gate,
2. Bon - net, bon - net, bon - net, bon - net,

Melody: 1. As I went up to Sand-gate, to Sand-gate, to Sand-gate,
2. He wears a blue bon-net, blue bon-net, blue bon-net,

Sand - gate, Sand-gate, I heard a las-sie sing:
bon - net, bon - net, A dim-ple in his chin.

As I went up to Sand-gate, I heard a las-sie sing:
A snow-white rose up-on it, A dim-ple in his chin.

Melody:

Oh, weel may the keel row, the keel row, the keel row,

Weel may the keel row, the keel row, the keel row,

(86)

Oh, weel may the keel row that my lad - die's in.

Weel may the keel row that my lad - die's in.

Keel row, keel row, keel row, keel row,

Melody: Weel may the keel row, the keel row, the keel row,

Keel row, keel row, that my lad - die's in.

Weel may the keel row that my lad - die's **in.**

Wraggle Taggle Gypsies

Traditional   NOTE   English Folk Song

Moderately

1. Three gyp-sies stood at the cas-tle gate;
2. They sang so sweet, they sang so shrill
3. She plucked off her high-heeled shoes

They sang so high, they sang so low;
That fast her tears be-gan to flow,
A-made of Span-ish leath-er, O

The la-dy sat in her cham-ber late,
And she laid down her silk-en gown,
She went in the street with her bare, bare feet,

Her heart it melt-ed a-way as snow.
Her gold-en rings and all her show.
All out in the wind and weath-er, O.

4. "Oh, saddle me my milk-white steed,
And go and fetch me my pony, O,
That I may ride and seek my bride,
Who's gone with the wraggle taggle gypsies, O!"

5. Oh, he rode high and he rode low,
He rode through wood and copses, too,
Until he came to an open field
And there he espied his-a lady, O.

6. "What makes you leave your house and land,
   Your golden treasures for to go?
   What makes you leave your new-wedded lord
   To follow the wraggle taggle gypsies, O?"

7. "What care I for my house and land?
   What care I for my treasure, O?
   What care I for my new-wedded lord?
   I'm off with the wraggle taggle gypsies, O!"

Kuckaburro

Traditional   NOTE   **Australian Round**

In strict time

Kuc - ka - bur - ro   up   in the   old gum   tree, —

Mer - ry, mer-ry   king   of the   bush   is   he; —

Laugh,   kuc - ka - bur - ro,   laugh,   kuc - ka - bur - ro!

Gay   your   life   must   be.

Kuckaburro is the laughing bird of Australia.

The Cardinal

Isabel Innes   NOTE   T. Tapper

Smoothly

1. "Friend - ly red song-ster, Oh, why are you here?
2. "Child at the win-dow, why grieve a-bout me?

Snow-flakes are fall - ing, cold win - ter is near;
Brav - ing cold weath - er, quite hap - py I'll be;

Birds south are fly - ing, In sun-shine to play, —
All thro' the win - ter I'll sing ev - 'ry day, —

Has - ten your jour-ney a - way, a - way!"
Here in my home-land I stay, I stay."

November Days

Translated NOTE French Folk Song

No-vem-ber days are here a-gain, The winds are chill and cold,

The gar-den once so gay and bright Looks with-ered, brown, and old.

The skies are dark and low-'ring, The trees they moan and sigh,

I hear the dry leaves whis-per-ing Of sum-mer long gone by.

Faith of Our Fathers

F. W. Faber NOTE Henry Hemy

Firmly

1. Faith of our fa - thers, liv - ing still
2. Faith of our fa - thers, we will love

Turn to page 235 for orchestra parts.

In spite of dun - geon, fire, and sword,
Both friend and foe in all our strife

Oh, how our hearts beat high with joy
And preach thee, too, as love knows how,

When-e'er we hear that glo - rious word!
By kind - ly words and vir - tuous life.

Faith of our fa - thers, ho - ly faith!

We will be true to thee till death.

Come, Ye Thankful People

Henry Alford NOTE G. J. Elvey

Joyfully

1. Come, ye thank-ful peo-ple, come, Raise the song of
2. All the world is God's own field, Fruit un-to His

har - vest home; All is safe - ly gath - ered in
praise to yield; Wheat and tares to - geth - er sown,

Ere the win - ter storms be - gin. God, our Mak - er,
Un - to joy or sor - row grown. First the blade and

doth pro - vide For our wants to be sup - plied;
then the ear, Then the full corn doth ap - pear;

Come to God's own tem-ple, come, Raise the song of har-vest home.
Lord of har-vest, grant that we Whole-some grain and pure may be.

Psalm 117

O praise the Lord, all ye nations: praise Him, all ye people.
For His merciful kindness is great toward us: and the truth of the
Lord endureth for ever. Praise ye the Lord.

The Trout

Translated from
C. F. D. Schubart

ROTE

Schubert

Moderately fast

1. In   yon-der brook-let stream-ing, Ap-
2. With   rod and silk line   run-ning, An

peared a   play - ful   trout;   Like some bright ar-row
an - gler came   that   way   And saw with cru-el

gleam - ing, It   dart - ed   in   and   out.   A -
cun - ning The   trout be - low him   play.   I

bove I watched with pleas - ure, Con - tent to lie and
turned my thoughts to wish - ing That   in   a   brook so

look At   such a   sil - ver treas - ure Go swim-ming in the
clear No lure would help the fish - ing, The trout would not go

brook; At   such   a   sil - ver   treas - ure Go
near; No   lure would help   the   fish - ing, The

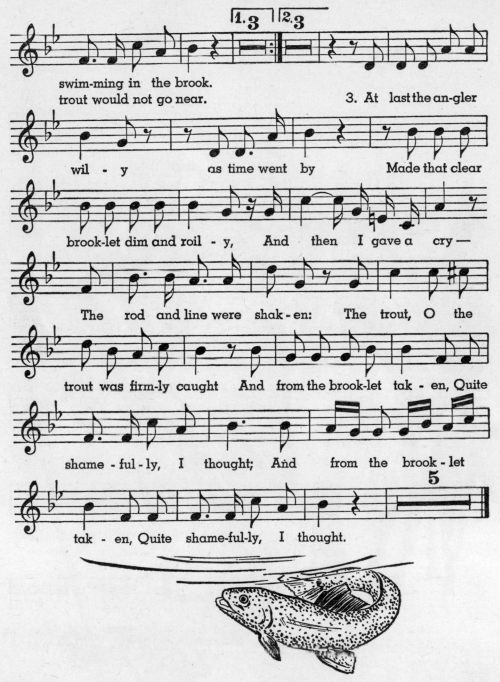

swim-ming in the brook.
trout would not go near.   3. At last the an-gler

wil - y   as time went by   Made that clear

brook-let dim and roil - y,   And   then   I gave a   cry —

The   rod and line were shak - en: The   trout, O the

trout was firm-ly caught   And from the brook-let tak - en, Quite

shame - ful - ly, I thought; And   from the   brook - let

tak - en, Quite shame-ful-ly, I thought.

Indian Culture

As you know, many years before the white man came to the Western Hemisphere another race of people inhabited parts of North, Central, and South America. These people were called Indians by the early European explorers, who thought that they had landed in the Indies although actually they had only reached the islands off the mainland of the then unknown continents of the Americas.

The so-called Indians are thought to be of common ancestry, Asiatic in character. One theory is that they first came across the Bering Sea from Asia to what is now Alaska and then gradually worked their way south and scattered over a vast territory. Through the centuries they became divided among many nations, with varying languages, customs, and cultures.

In North America the highest degree of civilization was reached in our Southwest. In Mexico the Aztecs (az'teks) developed a strong nation. In Central America the Mayas (mah'yahz) had their stronghold. In South America the Quechuas (kech'wahz) became organized into an empire ruled over by the Inca, or Sun God. The center of this ancient civilization was in Cuzco (koos'koh), high in an Andean valley in what is now the Republic of Peru. The people of the Incas were organized primarily as an agricultural nation. They also were skillful builders of highways, bridges, and great stone fortifications. They terraced the sides of the valleys to provide more land for farming and irrigated this land with water brought in aqueducts from the mountains. To the Indians we owe such important food crops as corn, potatoes, tomatoes, and chocolate. They were first grown in the New World.

Singing and dancing played an important part in the life of the Quechuas, who are sometimes called Incas. Great festivals were held at times of planting and harvesting. Many of the melodies persist to this day. They are usually based upon the pentatonic, or five-toned, scale and are danced, sung, and played. The principal instrument was flutelike and called a quena (kay'nah). It was sometimes made from the bone of an animal or carved out of stone. Often it was made from a hollow reed. There were also many varieties of percussion instruments. Later, possibly through the influence of the white man, stringed instruments were developed.

Reaping Song

Adapted   NOTE   Peruvian Indian
Harvest Dance

Gaily

Pip-ers play a lilt-ing tune, To thresh-ing floor the work-ers

call - ing. Cat - tle tramp the piles of wheat, To earth the

yel-low grain is fall - ing. Wom-en, fin-ished with their

mow - ing, To the floor the wheat are throw - ing.

Tossed high in air, gold-en straw all a-round is blow - ing.

The Shepherd

Paraphrased   NOTE   Peruvian Indian Song

Slowly

1. From a grass-y hill - side Pipes a shep - herd low - ly;
2. From a loft - y hill - side Pipes the shep - herd slow - ly;

For his flock he's blow - ing, To the val - ley go - ing.
Safe his flock he's lead - ing, To their win - ter feed - ing.

Hymn to the Sun

Paraphrased ROTE Ancient Inca Hymn

Majestically

1. To the ris - ing Sun God Morn-ing hymn we
2. To the ris - ing Sun God Morn-ing hymn we

raise! Great cre - a - tor of moun - tain and
raise! Light re - flect - ed by plan - et and

stream, Lord of na - ture and rul - er su-
moon, Light that burns in its full - ness at

preme, Thee, O Sun, we praise.
noon, Thee, O Sun, we praise.

This song sounds well when it is played on the flute.

(99)

The Cruel Shadow

Adapted   NOTE   Inca Melody

Very slowly

1. Far be-low the al-ti-plan-o, reach-ing bar-ren and drear,
2. I can hear a shep-herd call-ing by the riv-er-side clear,

Lie the green and qui-et mead-ows of my home-land. —
Far a-way the ech-oes fall-ing on my home-land. —

Con-dors great are fly-ing, o'er the val-leys ly-ing
An-gry winds are blow-ing, cold the wa-ters flow-ing

'Neath the moun-tains' cru-el shad-ow on my home-land. —
From the moun-tains' cru-el shad-ow on my home-land. —

An altiplano (ahl-teh-plah-noh) is a high plateau.

(100)

North American Indian Music

Indian music belongs to America, as it evolved here and was not transplanted from abroad. Its rhythmic stories are inseparable from Indian social life, for on every important occasion Indians sing and dance in groups. The drum beat regulates the movement, and the voice pulsates melodically. The body imitates the movements and gestures of whatever is being sung about. There is a sincere religious power in the words of Indian songs, even though the words are few. "White man's songs talk too much," says the Indian.

The rhythmic form of Indian music is not like ours. Even when it seems to fall into a strict four-four or two-four pattern, it quite suddenly seems to shrink or expand the time given to each individual beat for several measures. The commonest drum-beat patterns are:

1. A steady, even stroke, commonly unaccented.
2. Groups of unaccented short tones, somewhat like triplets.
3. A continuous small tremolo effect.
4. A single stroke followed by a softer, lighter stroke that seems to be the rebound from the impact with the drum head.

In the old days the Indian's instruments were of only two kinds: (1) percussive drums and rattles and (2) wind instruments. It is thought that originally a skin was laid on the ground and beaten with a stick. Later the drum was evolved from this crude practice. Still later the drums were painted and decorated. There are one-headed, light hand drums and there are two-headed drums of all sizes. The rattles are elaborately decorated. The wind instruments are flutes of various woods and sizes.

On the following pages you will find several Indian chants, written by Lew Sarett. These are printed with accent marks to show you how to read them in accordance with the actual rhythmic flow of the words. A few boys and girls may use drum beats to accompany the chanting.

Thunderdrums

Translated
Lew Sarett

ROTE

Chippewa War Dance

I

Rhythm of words
Drum beats and
accents

Beat on the buckskin, beat on the drums,

Hi! Hi! Hi! for the Thunderbird comes;

His eyes burn red with the blood of battle;

His wild wings roar in the medicine rattle.

Thunderbird-god, while our spirits dance,

Tip with your lightning the warrior's lance;

On shafts of wind, with heads of flame,

Build for us arrows that torture and maim;

Ho! may our ironwood war clubs crash

With a thunderbolt head and a lightning flash.

Hi! Hi! Hi! hear the cut-throat's doom

As our wild bells ring and our thunderdrums boom.

II

An Indian called Double Bear dances:

Hi! Hi! Hi!

My wild feet fly,

For I follow the track

Of a cowardly pack;

Footprints here,

Footprints there,

Enemies near!

Taint in the air!

Signs on the sod!

Ho! the Thunderbird-god

Gives me the eye

Of a hawk in the sky!

Beat, beat on the drums,

For the Thunderbird comes.

Ho! Ho!

Ho! Ho!

The Blue Duck

Translated
Lew Sarett

ROTE   Chippewa Medicine Dance

This chant is also a Chippewa medicine-dance ceremonial. In the early autumn the tribe gathers in a dancing ring near a lake to place upon a pole a blue duck carved from wood. As Mr. Sarett describes it, "The ceremony is begun by the drummers, who beat monotonously upon the drums. The singers and the dancers then begin to stamp and to shout and to grunt, and finally to dance. The chief medicine men, who by virtue of their powerful medicine songs are thought to have supernatural power in influencing the spirits with which the earth, the sea, and the sky are inhabited, invoke Keetchie Manido, 'The Big Spirit,' to send down from the north a big flight of ducks for the fall hunt."

Rhythm of words
Drum beats and
accents

Hi-yee! Hi-yee! Blow on Ab-bi-too-bi plenty duck!

Ho!   Plenty, plenty duck!

Ho!   Plenty duck, plenty duck!

Ho!   Ho!

Hi! Hi! Hi! Hi!   Hi! Hi! Hi! Hi!

Hee — ya! — Hoi — ya! —

Hee — ya! — Hoi — ya! —

Keetchie Manido, Manido, —

I place this pretty duck upon your hand;

Upon its sunny palm and in its windy fingers.

Hi-yee! Blue and beautiful

Is he,   beautifully blue!

(Faster, louder, with a vigorous lilting beat)

Hi!   And seasoned many moons, many moons,

Ho!   Seasoned many, many, many sleeps!

Hi-yee! Blue and beautiful

Is he,   beautifully blue!

Though his throat is choked with wood,

And he honks not on his pole,

And his wings are weak with hunger,

Yet his heart is plenty good.

Hi-yee! His heart is plenty good!

Hi-yee! Plenty good, plenty good!

Hi-yee! Hi-yee! Hi-yee! His heart is good!

(Brokenly and brusquely)

My heart like his is good!
Ugh! My tongue talks straight!
Ho!

Indian Names

G. F. McKay   NOTE   G. F. McKay

Kootenai = koo-te-nay   Zuni = zoo-nee
Navajo = nav-e-hoh   Paiute = pie-ut
Guillayute = gill-ah-yoot

O Saviour Sweet

Translated   NOTE   Folk Tune used by Bach

Reverently

1. O Sav - iour sweet, O Sav - iour mild,
2. O Sav - iour sweet, O Sav - iour kind,

Who came to earth a lit - tle child,
A way to serve You we would find;

Your bless - ing send from heav'n a - bove
We'll fol - low You wher - e'er you guide

And bring to men good will and love,
That truth and kind - ness may a - bide,

O Sav - iour sweet, O Sav - iour mild.
O Sav - iour sweet, O Sav - iour kind.

(107)

Cherry Tree Carol

Traditional   ROTE   Early American Ballad

Smoothly, in time

1. As Mar - y and Jo - seph were a-
2. Then Mar - y spoke to Jo - seph so
3. Lord Je - sus spoke a few words all

walk - ing the green, There were ap - ples and
meek and so mild: "Jo-seph, gath - er me some
down un - to them: "Bow down, you loft - y

cher - ries a - plen-ty to be seen; There were
cher - ries for me and my child; Jo - seph,
cher-ry trees, let Mar-y gath - er some; Bow

ap - ples and cher - ries a - plen-ty to be seen."
gath-er me some cher - ries for me and my child."
down, you loft - y cher-ry trees, let Mar-y gath-er some."

4. The cherry trees bowed low down,
   Low down to the ground,
   And Mary gathered cherries
   While Joseph stood around.

5. Then Joseph took Mary
   All on his right knee.
   "Pray tell me, Lord Jesus,
   When your birthday will be."

6. "On old Christmas morning
   My birthday shall be,
   When the hills and high mountains
   Shall bow unto me."

(108)

Beth'lem Night

Paraphrased   ROTE   Catalan Carol

Fast, well accented

1-2. O - ver sleep-ing Beth-'lem town, zing zoom zoom zoom,

Moon and stars were shin - ing down, zing zoom zoom zoom.

1. Thro' the qui - et of the night, Just be - fore the morn-ing
2. In a rude and hum-ble stall There was born to save us

light, Far a - way the cocks were crow-ing; In their
all Ba-by Je - sus, Son of Mar - y, Mor - tal

sta - bles cat - tle low - ing, zoom zoom zoom.
sin and grief to car - ry, zoom zoom zoom.

March of the Three Kings

Translated   ROTE   Provencal Air

In marching rhythm

Yes - ter morn I met up-on their way The three great

kings of the O - rient rid - ing; Yes - ter

morn I met up-on their way The three great

End

kings in their bright ar - ray. And in their

train came a host un - told Of sol - diers

march - ing and pag - es proud - ly bear - ing

(110)

The in - cense rare and the gifts of gold

Go to the beginning.

To lay be - fore the feet of Christ, the King.

On the repeat, sing the first section as a round.

Mary's Lullaby

Adapted   NOTE   Polish Folk Song

Tenderly

1. Lull - a - by, ba - by, and sweet be your sleep-ing,
2. Rock - a - by, ba - by, poor shep-herds are near-ing,

Moth - er is hold-ing you, safe vig - il keep - ing;
Wise men from dis - tant lands now are ap - pear - ing;

Lull - a - by, ba - by, my own lit - tle trea - sure,
Rock - a - by, ba - by, the star shines a - bove you,

An - gels watch o - ver my joy with - out meas-ure.
Guid - ing the pil-grims who wor - ship and love you.

(111)

He Shall Feed His Flock

From the Bible   ROTE   Handel

Steady, with motion

He shall feed His flock like a

shep - herd, and He shall gath - er the

lambs with His arm, with His arm.

And car - ry them

in His bos - om, and gen - tly lead

those that are with young, and

gen - tly lead those, and gen - tly

lead   those   that   are   with young.

George Frederick Handel (1685-1759), a German composer who lived in England for many years, wrote religious dramas called "oratorios." An oratorio is always sung without action or stage settings. This song is from "The Messiah," an oratorio which requires several hours for performance. "Israel in Egypt," "Saul," and "Judas Maccabaeus" are other famous oratorios of Handel's.

Lullaby

ROTE   Mexican Folk Song

Translated

Tranquilly

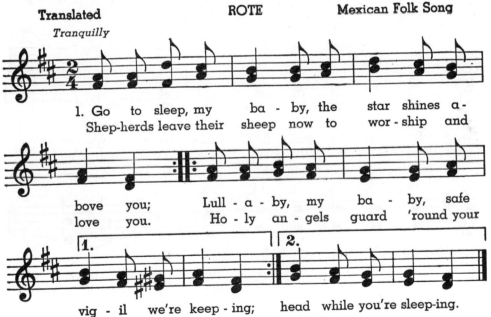

1. Go to sleep, my ba-by, the star shines a-
Shep-herds leave their sheep now to wor-ship and

bove you; Lull-a-by, my ba-by, safe
love you. Ho-ly an-gels guard 'round your

1.
vig-il we're keep-ing;

2.
head while you're sleep-ing.

2. Go to sleep, my baby, the heavens are ringing,
Gifts of priceless beauty the Wise Men are bringing;
Lullaby, my baby, safe vigil we're keeping;
Holy angels guard 'round your head while you're sleeping.

(113)

Song of the Infant Jesus

Paraphrased   ROTE   Chilean Tonada

In flowing rhythm

1. Long years a - go in Ju - de - a, —
2. Shep-herds came by to a - dore Him, —
3. An - gels in cho - rus were sing - ing, —

God gave a Son to Ma - ri - a, —
Knelt in the sta - ble be - fore Him, —
Peace on earth joy - ful - ly bring - ing, —

Je - sus, the gen - tle and ho - ly, —
Kings of the O - rient were near - ing, —
Prais - ing, that night in Ju - de - a, —

Friend to the poor and the low - ly. —
Led by a great star ap - pear - ing. —
Je - sus, the Son of Ma - ri - a. —

In Spanish the first verse is:

Cuando la Virgen María
Dío a luz el Niño de Dios,
Tan hermoso que nació
Que al mundo causo armonía.

Pilgrim's Song

Paraphrased · ROTE · Mexican Folk Song

Slowly

1. "Wak-en, O land-lord, I beg you, pray tell me,
2. "Hark-en, O pil-grim, in sor-row I tell you,

Have you a shel-ter for two pil-grims wea-ry?
There is no room in my inn I can give you.

Jour-neyed have we from ris - ing sun, Now the dark
Shel-ter you'll find in sta - ble yon, Fit for the

shad-ows of cold —— night creep on." ——
bed of a poor —— pil - grim's son." ——

The Spanish Christmas lasts from December 16 to January 6. In Mexico the boys and girls go through the streets in groups in the evening, carrying lighted candles and singing as they go. For nine days they seek admittance into the houses, but it is not until the twenty-fifth of December that they are allowed to enter.

The boys and girls then sing their favorite carols before the altar which is in every home. They also break the piñata, a large thin clay vase which hangs from the ceiling. It is covered with colored tissue-paper representations of flowers and fruits or animals and people. One of the children is blindfolded, given a stick, and told to break the piñata open. He is guided by the cries of encouragement or discouragement of the crowd. When he finally succeeds in break-ing it open, a shower of candies, nuts, and fruit tumbles down.

Villancico

Translated   ROTE   Argentine Folk Song

1. Tell me, Ma-
2. Sweet sounds the

ri - a, In good - ness, I pray: Oh,
tim - brel With clear ring - ing tone; We

Who is the Ba - by new - born to - day?
sing glad ho - san - nas to God's own Son.

Farmer's Song

Translated NOTE Chinese Work Song

Rhythmically

1. All walk a-long and swing the hoe, nah! Chop all the
2. See how the green stems bend and sway, nah! Soft-ly the

weeds in ev-'ry row, nah! Ee yah heh!
breez-es o'er them play, nah! Ee yah heh!

Ee yah heh! So the plants may grow. —
Ee yah heh! Thro' the ear-ly day. —

Ee yah heh! — Ee yah heh! — Ya ho heh!
Ee yah heh! — Ee yah heh! — Ya ho heh!

3. Gentle the rain as sun rides high,
   Sprouting the seeds beneath the sky,
   Swing your hoe and cry.

4. Bring all the men from far and near,
   Cut ev'ry stalk and golden ear,
   Harvest time is here.

5. Gather the corn and thresh the wheat,
   Store all the grain that folk may eat,
   Grain is farmers' meat.

Chinese Lullaby

Unknown   ROTE   Based on a Chinese scale

Chi-nese sand-man, wise and creep-y, Croon dream song to

make us sleep - y.   Chi - nese maid with   dark - brown eyes,

Queen of all their lull - a-bies, On her an-cient moon gui-tar

Strums a "sleep song" to   a star;   When big Chi - nese

Go to the beginning.

shad - ows fall,   Snow-white lil - ies   hear   her call.

Song of the Pigeon

Translated   ROTE   Bengali Folk Song

Rather fast, well accented

1. Pi-geons soar-ing, gen - tly coo-ing un - der az - ure sky, —
2. High a - bove us wood-en cas-es I've se - cure - ly tied, —
3. Ev -'ry morn-ing bright and ear-ly, bowl of rice in hand, —

Up-ward, for-ward, down-ward swoop-ing, in great cir-cles fly. —
Placed where all my wea-ry fly-ers safe-ly home may glide. —
I will scat-ter grain while call-ing for my pi-geon band. —

1-3. Bak-ba kum kum, bak-ba kum kum, bak-ba kum kum, bak. —

My Island

Adapted   NOTE   Philippine Folk Song

In swinging rhythm

1. The sun is ris-ing high a-bove the
2. The sea comes rid-ing o'er the reef with
3. The gen-tle breez-es car-ry on the

moun-tains green — To light a crown of
spar-kling foam — A-long the cor-al
soft warm air — The scent of fruit and

beau-ty — up-on my is-land queen. —
beach-es — a-round my is-land home. —
blos-soms — thro' all my is-land fair. —

Turn to page 237 for orchestra parts.

Maranoa Lullaby

Translated   NOTE   Australian Aboriginal Song

Sleep as falls the dark   In your bed of bark; None shall harm you, dear,
Hm ———————   Hm ——————— Hm ———————

Moth-er watch-es near,   Hm ———————

Mafulu War Song

Papuan   ROTE   Papuan Song from New Guinea

E! E! E! Si-

vu mam-bu-la ju ju   la —   e-mu je ka le

Repeat indefinitely.

"E" is pronounced "ay." The other syllables are pronounced as they are spelled.

The Nile

Adapted   ROTE   Based on a Nile Chant

Smoothly

Ma - bah - lay - o! —   Ma - bah - lay - o! —

O thou might - y riv - er, moth - er of all,

Far' in dis - tant re - gion spring - ing, Thro' yon fer - tile val - ley

sing - ing, Flow a - long, bless-ed your song, Wa - ter to E - gypt

bring - ing, Ma - bah - lay - o! —————— Ma-

bah-lay - o! ——— Ma-bah - lay - o! ———

Keys in Major and Minor Modes

In *The American Singer, Book Four,* you were given the rule for locating *do:*

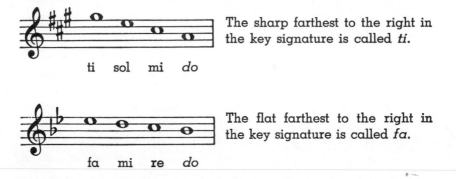

ti   sol   mi   *do*

The sharp farthest to the right in the key signature is called *ti.*

fa   mi   re   *do*

The flat farthest to the right in the key signature is called *fa.*

Now, if you can locate *do* and if you know the pitch names of the lines and spaces of the staff, as given on page 36, you will be able to name the keynote of every song you sing.

NAMING THE KEYS

MAJOR MODE

Do is the keynote in the major mode. Instead of calling it by the syllable *do,* call it by its letter name:

do—F   do—G

If a flat is on the same line or space as *do,* name the key with the flat:

do—B♭   do—E♭

Here are the keys in the major mode that are most often used:

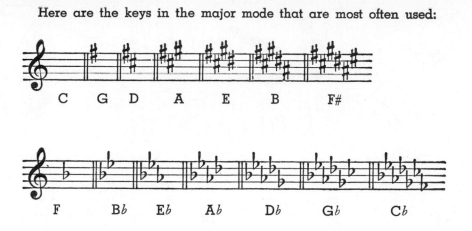

C G D A E B F#

F B♭ E♭ A♭ D♭ G♭ C♭

MINOR MODE

La is the keynote in the minor mode. Instead of calling it by that syllable, call it by its letter name:

la—d   la—e

Here are the keys in the minor mode:

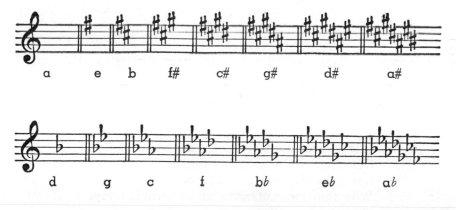

a e b f# c# g# d# a#

d g c f b♭ e♭ a♭

Cradle Song

Translated   NOTE   Armenian Slumber Song

1. Night-in-gale, come wing-ing,   leave the gar-den wild,
2. Dove-kin, leave your pi-geons   ly-ing in the nest,
3. Nois-y, thiev-ing mag-pie,   cheer my lit-tle one,

Bring a gen-tle   sleep song   to my fret-ful   child!
With your dole-ful   coo-ing   lull my babe to   rest!
Sing to him of   rich-es,   prof-its to be   won!

No, my son is   cry-ing;   stay, my night-in-gale, —
Still my son is   weep-ing;   dove-kin, fly a-way, —
Yet he cries; old mag-pie,   to your thick-et flee, —

For he'll be no   min-strel,   gay with song or   tale.
He will be no   mourn-er   in the com-ing   day.
For my son a   trades-man   does not care to   be.

4. Falcon, brave and warlike, leave your helpless prey;
Here, perhaps, my darling wants your song today!
Now my son is silent; to the mountain keep;
With your songs of battle, off he went to sleep.

(124)

The Nine Girls

Translated   NOTE   Alsatian Game Song

Gaily

1. There were nine girls in fa-ther's care, There were nine
2. One day the Prince we danced to meet, One day the
3. All of the daugh-ters he would wed, All of the

girls in fa-ther's care; All of the nine were young and
Prince we danced to meet; All of the nine he came to
daugh-ters he would wed; But he ran off with one in-

fair, All of the nine were young and fair. There was Ma-
greet, All of the nine he came to greet, Bowed to Ma-
stead, But he ran off with one in-stead. There was Ma-

rie, there was A - mie, Then there were Bess and Tess and
rie, bowed to A - mie, Then there were Bess and Tess and
rie, there was A - mie, Then there were Bess and Tess and

1—3. Jess, Ju - dy tall and Tru - dy small, There was wit - ty Ju - li-

a, There was pret - ty blonde An-gel - i - ca. —
a, But he kissed the blonde An-gel - i - ca. —
a, But he mar-ried blonde An-gel - i - ca. —

Come to the Land

Adapted   NOTE   Rumanian Folk Dance

Come to the land with joy and with spir - it,

Slide on R.   *Slide on L.*

Come to our na - tive land; Come to the land with

Run back.   *Hop R.*   *Step L.*

joy and with spir - it, Come to our na - tive land.

Step L, R.   *Repeat all steps.*

We have plowed the fields and have plant - ed grain,

We have plowed the fields and have plant-ed grain,

We'll reap a might-y har-vest, We'll reap a might-y har - vest.

Repeat all steps.

The "hora" is a group dance for as many as wish to join in the circle. The dancers stand side by side with their hands resting on the shoulders of the persons to the right and the left. The dance is only six measures long and is repeated continuously with a gradual acceleration until it is very fast and exciting, usually ending in a shout.

The pattern is as follows; M stands for measure:

M 1. *Slide forward and hop on the right foot, raising the left foot backward.*
M 2. *Slide forward and hop on the left foot, raising the right foot backward.*
M 3-4. *Do a running step backward on the right, left, right foot, and hop on the right foot, kicking the left foot forward.*

The circle now moves sideward with long running steps:

M 5. *Step sideward left with the left foot, crossing the right foot in the rear.*
M 6. *Step sideward left on the left foot and hop on the left foot, swinging the right foot forward in a little kick. Step sideward on the right foot and swing the left foot forward in a kick.*

The syncopation pattern is:

Beat

A Rune

Paraphrased   NOTE   Ancient Finnish Tune

1. Broth-ers, join our tri-bal sing-ing, Tell-ing o'er the old-en sto - ry,

All our an-cient leg-ends bring-ing, All our tale of by-gone glo - ry.

2. Songs our honored fathers taught us,
   From the mystic runes beginning,
   Tales our gentle mothers brought us,
   By the fireside deftly spinning.

3. Songs the western winds came blowing,
   As on giant harp strings playing,
   Murmured by the waters, flowing,
   Whispered thro' the tree tops, swaying.

4. Legends of the field and meadow,
   Chanted oft by Wai-na-moi-nen,
   Minstrel of the Kalevala,
   Known thro' all the mighty Northland.

The Kalevala (kah-lay-vah-lah) of the Finnish people is one of the oldest heroic poems known to man. It was transmitted from century to century through a form of chanting. Longfellow's poem "Hiawatha" is said to be patterned after the rhythm of the Kalevala.

Four Faces

J. W. Beattie   ROTE   J. W. Beattie

Firmly

O'er the Black Hills of South Da - ko - ta, on a

moun - tain's gran-ite face, There are carved the heads of

four great men which time can - not e - rase. From the

val - leys, plains, and high - ways you can see these heads a-

far, While the coun - try round seems light - ed up as

by some bea-con star. — And the four men of hon-ored

sto - ry   in our mem - o - ries be - long   Like the

rock from which their fac - es shine un - shak - en, firm and strong.

My Homeland

Paraphrased   NOTE   Slovak Folk Song

Vigorously

For-ests of ma-ple on   hill - sides green, Moun-tain-tops reach-ing the

sky   se - rene,   Gay flow-ered mead-ows, broad sweep-ing val - leys,

Or-chards and grain fields on   ev - 'ry hand,   Riv-ers ma-jes - tic,

swift-run-ning stream-lets—There is my coun-try,   my own dear land.

By the Fireside

Adapted   ROTE   Schumann

Moderately fast

At night by the fire-side when the lights are low, I

see strange pic-tures form-ing in the em - bers' glow; Some-

growing louder

times a scene from dis - tant plac - es seems to move quite near;

And then at oth-er times the fac-es of my friends ap-pear.

There in the shad-ows when the lights are low, I

see strange pic-tures form-ing in the em - bers' glow.

Robert Schumann wrote this melody as part of his piano composition called "Scenes from Childhood."

Song for Freedom

Translated   NOTE   Russian Folk Song

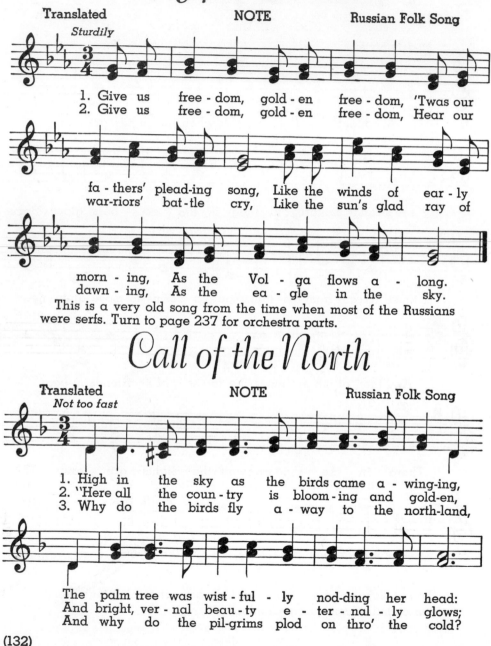

Sturdily

1. Give us free-dom, gold-en free-dom, 'Twas our
2. Give us free-dom, gold-en free-dom, Hear our

fa-thers' plead-ing song, Like the winds of ear-ly
war-riors' bat-tle cry, Like the sun's glad ray of

morn-ing, As the Vol-ga flows a-long.
dawn-ing, As the ea-gle in the sky.

This is a very old song from the time when most of the Russians were serfs. Turn to page 237 for orchestra parts.

Call of the North

Translated   NOTE   Russian Folk Song

Not too fast

1. High in the sky as the birds came a-wing-ing,
2. "Here all the coun-try is bloom-ing and gold-en,
3. Why do the birds fly a-way to the north-land,

The palm tree was wist-ful-ly nod-ding her head:
And bright, ver-nal beau-ty e-ter-nal-ly glows;
And why do the pil-grims plod on thro' the cold?

"Why leave the com-fort and warmth of our sun-shine
Ne'er does the sun hide be - hind clouds for - bid-ding,
"There in the north are our for - ests and grain fields,

And fly to the still fro - zen north-land in - stead?"
As fear - ful of frost or of deep win - ter snows."
Our own lov - ed home-land that calls as of old."

Winter by the Dnieper

Translated   NOTE   Ukrainian Folk Song

Slowly

1. I - ci - ly cold the Dnie-per rag-es, Bit-ter the
2. Fu-rious-ly cold the Dnie-per rag-es, Som-ber and

winds as on they pass; Touch-ing the ground, the weep - ing
dark the storm clouds blow; Vil - lag-es lie in si - lent

wil-lows, Freez-ing the steppes and mead - ow grass.
slum-ber, Bur - ied be - neath the drift - ed snow.

The Dnieper (nee-per) is the second longest river in Russia. For most of its 1300-mile course it flows through rich grain land.

The Troika

Translated   NOTE   Russian Popular Song

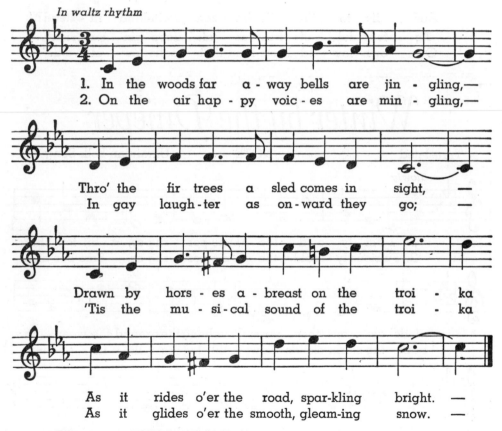

In waltz rhythm

1. In the woods far a-way bells are jin - gling,—
2. On the air hap - py voic - es are min - gling,—

Thro' the fir trees a sled comes in sight, —
In gay laugh-ter as on-ward they go; —

Drawn by hors - es a - breast on the troi - ka
'Tis the mu - si-cal sound of the troi - ka

As it rides o'er the road, spar-kling bright. —
As it glides o'er the smooth, gleam-ing snow. —

Turn to page 236 for orchestra parts.

Tschaikowsky (1840-1893) wrote an interesting composition called "The Troika," or "The Three-Horse Sleigh," in which there are the sounds of sleigh bells. Perhaps you can listen to a recording of it.

The Terek

Translated   ROTE   Russian Folk Song

Rapidly

Danc-ing a-long the rock - y paths of the great moun-tain,

Fu-rious-ly runs the Te - rek; Drop-ping a-way like gi - ant

tears in a deep foun-tain, Nois-i - ly runs the Te - rek;

Thro' wood-lands go - ing, By fields of grain flow - ing,

O - ver the rap - ids splash-ing, On to the plains dash-ing,

Surg-ing with wave-like mo - tion. "Take me," the stream is call - ing,

Wea-ry at last, fall - ing Safe in the in - land o - cean.

The Terek (tya-rek) is a tempestuous river that rises in the Cau-
casus Mountains. Like the Volga, it flows into the Caspian Sea.

The triplet ♪♪♪ is sung on one beat.

Our Flag

H. W. Loomis   NOTE   A. E. Johnstone

With spirit

1. White, like the clouds a-bove; Blue, like the sky; And
2. Lights, like the morn-ing stars, Shine thro' its fleece; The

1. White, like the clouds a-bove; Blue, like the
2. Lights, like the morn-ing stars, Shine thro' its

red as ris - ing sun our flag waves high. The
pow - er of their glo - ry ne'er shall cease. Our

sky; And red as ris - ing sun, our flag waves
fleece; The pow-er of their glo - ry ne'er shall

Ban - ner of the Right, The Sym - bol of
Stand-ard be se - cure While a - ges en-

high. The Ban - ner of the Right, The
cease. Our Stand-ard be se - cure While

Light O'er the town and the coun-try-side
dure, Giv-ing hon - or with e - qual rights,

Sym - bol of Light O'er the town and the
a - ges en - dure, Giv-ing hon - or with

1.

2.

Gleams from the height.
Free - dom and peace. Hur - rah! —

coun - try from the height.
e - qual rights and peace. Hur - rah! —

The Children's Prayer

Translated   ROTE   Humperdinck
Reverently

p

When at night I go to sleep, Four-teen an-gels

p

When at night I go to sleep, Four-teen an-gels

(137)

round me creep, Two my head com - mand - ing,

watch to keep Two my head are guard - ing

round me creep, Two my head com - mand - ing,

mp

Two be-low me stand - ing, Two my right se-

Two my feet are guid ing Two are on my

Two be-low me stand - ing,

lect - ing, Two my left pro-tect - ing,

right hand Two are on my left hand

mp

Two my right se - lect - ing, Two my left pro-

Two give me cov - er, Two o'er me

Two who warmly cov - er *Two who o'er me* (tect - ing, Two give me cov - er,)

hov - er, Two near me bid - ing, My

hov - er *Two to whom 'tis giv - en to* (Two o'er me hov - er, Two my heav'n-ly)

heav'n-ly jour - ney guid - ing.

guide my steps to *hea - ven* (jour - ney guid - ing.)

The Sailor Maid

Paraphrased　　　　　　　　NOTE　　　　Netherlands Folk Song

In swinging rhythm

1. Once a maid was work-ing at sea, Dressed as a sail - or,
2. When a storm came o - ver the deck, Off went the fore - jib,
3. "O my cap - tain, lis - ten to me! I am your daugh-ter,

no-bod - y knew her; Stowed a - way, her voy - age be - gan,
miz-zen and spank-er; Fore and aft our her - o - ine ran,
help me a - way, sir!" "Put for shore as fast as you can,

Try - ing the life of a real sail - ing man.
No long - er try - ing to act like a man.
Sail - ing a ship is a job for a man."

Tilda Jane and Samuel

L. S. Rushing　　　　　　NOTE　　　　Grace V. Wilson

In steady rhythm

Girls 1. Who's that rid - ing by our door, Sam - uel Dunn?
Girls 2. Hear him shout-ing at our door, Sam - uel Dunn?
All 3. Who's that rid - ing by your door, Sam - uel Dunn?

On the third stanza, the boys sing their melody against that of the girls, as in a two-part song.

Who's that rid-ing by our door, Sam-uel Dunn?
Hear him shout-ing at our door, Sam-uel Dunn?
Who's that rid-ing by your door, Sam-uel Dunn?

Like a hom-ing bird in flight He is rid-ing thro' the night,
If you love your na-tive land, Get your gun and read-y stand,
Oh, they're he-roes brave and true Who have died for me and you,

Who's that rid-ing by our door,— Sam-uel Dunn?
Hear him shout-ing at our door,— Sam-uel Dunn?
Who's that rid-ing by your door,— Sam-uel Dunn?

Boys Why, he's knock-ing at our door, Til-da Jane!
Boys Who's that rid-ing from your door, Til-da Jane?
All Who's that rid-ing by your door, Til-da Jane?

Why, he's knock-ing at our door, Til-da Jane!
Who's that rid-ing from your door, Til-da Jane?
Who's that rid-ing by your door, Til-da Jane?

O it's Neigh-bor Paul Re-vere, And he's shout-ing loud and clear,
It's your brave and no-ble man, He will help wher-e'er he can,
O they're he-roes brave and true Who have died for me and you,

Yes, he's shout-ing at our door,— Til-da Jane!
He will take a he-ro's stand,— Til-da Jane!
They are rid-ing by your door,— Til-da Jane!

Freight Boats

James Tippett   ROTE   J. Wolverton

Moderately fast, well accented

1. Boats that car-ry   sug-ar and to - bac-co from Ha - van - a,
2. Boats like box-es   load-ed down with tons of sand and grav - el,

Boats that car-ry   co - co - nuts and   cof-fee from Bra - zil,
Boats with blocks of gran-ite for a   build-ing on   the hill,

Boats that car - ry   cot-ton from the   cit - y of Sa - van-nah,
Boats that meas-ure man-y lone-some   miles   of   trav - el,

Boats that car-ry   an - y - thing from an - y place you will.
Boats that car-ry   an - y - thing from an - y place you will.

The Fountain

Translated   ROTE   Italian Folk Song
from Abruzzi

With flowing motion

1. O how fresh and pure the rip-pling, chat-ter-ing foun-tain!
2. O how fresh and pure the rip-pling, chat-ter-ing foun-tain!

Wa-ter clear as crys-tal from the tow-er-ing moun-tain,
Wa-ter clear as crys-tal from the tow-er-ing moun-tain,

Deep in rock - bound cav - erns spring - ing,
Past green fields with vi - 'lets grow - ing,

Spar - kling, bab - bling, gai - ly sing - ing,
Laugh - ing, sing - ing, gai - ly flow - ing,

Oh, what price - less jew - els bring - ing,
Oh, what price - less jew - els show - ing,

As you glit - ter in the sun. —
As you glit - ter in the sun.

(143)

Lovely Meadows

Translated   NOTE   Czech Folk Song

Joyfully

1. O love-ly mead-ows, rich and fair,
2. Home to our val-leys, green and wide,

High the grass is grow-ing, High the grass is grow-ing;
We will go to-geth-er, We will go to-geth-er;

O love-ly mead-ows, rich and fair,
Home to our val-leys, green and wide,

Spoken

High the grass is grow-ing ev-'ry-where. Hey!
We will go to-geth-er, side by side. Hey!

Wa-ters of melt-ed snow From dis-tant moun-tains flow,

Cir-cling a-round they go, Close by the ma-ple tree;

Turn to page 238 for orchestra parts.

Wa - ters of melt-ed snow From dis - tant moun-tains flow,

Spoken

Cir - cling a - round they go, Call-ing for me. Hey!

Flow, River

Paraphrased   ROTE   Slovak Folk Song

Slowly

1. Riv - er si - lent-ly flow By my vil - lage fair,
2. Riv - er, la - zi - ly sweep By my child-hood home,

Whis - per low as you go; How I would be there!
Tell her now that I weep As a - far I roam.

O'er the Horizon

Translated   NOTE   Serbian Folk Song

Slowly

1. O'er the ho - ri - zon, Be-yond the set - ting sun, —
2. O'er the ho - ri - zon, Be-yond the dis - tant sea, —

My lit-tle vil-lage is sleep - ing, Si - lent as day is done. —
Friend-ly com-pan-ions are wait-ing, There where I long to be. —

(145)

Samiotissa

Translated   NOTE   Greek Folk Song
from the Isle of Samos

1. Sa - mio - tis-sa, Sa - mio - tis-sa, Far be-yond our is-land you
2. Sa - mio - tis-sa, Sa - mio - tis-sa, From our shore you jour-neyed a-

roam; Sa - mio - tis - sa, Sa - mio - tis-sa, When will you be com-ing back
way; Sa - mio - tis - sa, Sa - mio - tis-sa, Soon you'll be re-turn-ing to

home?   For   a hap-py wel-come, the   fig   and ol - ive blos-som
stay.   For the home-ward voy-age I've built   a stur - dy ves - sel

Strew their pet - als o'er the   land.   What a cheer-ful greet-ing as
Bright with flags of ev - 'ry   hue.   Sails of gold-en can-vas and

friend and neigh-bor scat-ter crim-son ros - es   on   the   sand!
oars   of flash - ing sil - ver bring you o'er the wa-ters   blue!

Themes

Adapted   ROTE   Smetana

In swinging rhythm

In dis - tant hills there springs the clear Mol - dau,

Thro' green for-ests mur - mur-ing a gay, rip - pling song.

Theme in E Minor

Quite fast

By Pra-ha's gold-en spires the broad Mol - dau flows, the

Mol - dau flows; A proud, might-y riv-er, she goes sweep-ing a-

long; A proud, might-y riv-er, she goes sweep-ing a - long.

Theme in E Major

Frederick Smetana (1824-1884), a Bohemian composer, wrote music depicting the beauties of his native country. In "The Moldau" he painted a picture in tone of Bohemia's principal river. These two themes are from "The Moldau."

The Bagpipers

Paraphrased ROTE Czech Dance Tune

A A'

1. Bag-pipes sound-ing near the vil-lage
2. Bag-pipes sound-ing near the vil-lage

Waa Waa Waa Waa

Lure me with their wail-ing call, There's the chim-ney
Lead the march-ers on their way; Smith and butch-er,

Waa Waa Waa

sweep who beck-ons, Him I do not like at all.
sweep and tail-or, Home a-gain they'll come some day.

Waa Waa Waa Waa

There's a tail - or   I   like best,   For,   more hand - y
Still the tail - or   I   pre -fer,   He's a   clev - er

Waa   Waa   Waa

than   the rest,   He   will   sew   for   me   a   bod - ice,
man - a -ger;   From   a - far   he'll   bring a   jack - et

Waa   Waa   Waa

Broi - dered,   for   my   wed - ding   chest.
Made   of   bor - rowed   rab - bit   fur.

Waa   Waa   Waa

Two clarinets may play the lower parts, transposed to the key of A.

Go On, Train

Zana Henderson   ROTE   Zana Henderson

Lazily

1. Some - thin' on the rail an' it ain't no liz - ard,
2. Some - thin' on the rail an' it ain't no liz - ard,

Woo - oo - oo - oo - oo - oo - oo! Start-in' for the north, where the
Woo - oo - oo - oo - oo - oo - oo! Here I got e-nough for to

winds make bliz-zard. Woo - oo - oo - oo - oo - oo - oo!
fill my giz-zard. Woo - oo - oo - oo - oo - oo - oo!

But I'm goin' to stay in the slow sun - shine,
So keep on the way where you're roll - in' to,

Ain't goin' a - way from this shack of mine, From my
Ain't goin' to lay off to ride with you, An' I'll

black - eyed peas an' my ba - con rind, From my
be right here 'neath a sky all blue, Where the

ta -ters an' my pos - sum an' my wa - ter - mel - on vine.
mock - in' birds are sing - in' just as sweet as hon - ey - dew!

Go on, train! Woo-oo-oo-oo-oo-oo-oo-oo! Woo-oo-oo-oo-oo-oo-oo-oo!

Betsy from Pike

Kansas Version   NOTE   Song of the "Forty-niners"

Brightly

1. Oh, have you heard tell of sweet Bet - sy from Pike,
2. They swum the deep riv - ers and clumb the high peaks,

Who crossed the wide prai - rie with old Un - cle Ike,
They rolled thro' the coun - try for man - y long weeks,

With two head of cat - tle and one spot - ted hog,
Thro' all sorts of mis - er - y, dry days and wet;

A tall Shang-hai roos - ter and one yel - low dog?
If they had - n't gone on, they'd be camp - in' there yet.

too - roo - lee   too - roo - lay

Chorus

Too - roo - lee ———— too - roo - lay ————
roo - lee   roo - lee   roo - lee - ay!

Sing - in' too -roo - lee,   too - roo - lee,   too - roo - lee - ay!

3. They came to the desert and salt-water lakes,
   The ground it was teemin' with varmints and snakes;
   Beset by wild Injuns, Comanche and Sioux,
   'Tis a marvelous tale how they ever got thro'.

4. One day as the morning was rosy and bright,
   They saw in the distance a wonderful sight;
   The end of the trail was so powerful near
   That they shouted, "Hurray, Californy, we're here!"

Winter

J. W. Beattie   NOTE   J. Wolverton

Moderately

1. Cold   from the   north   hear the winds of win-ter blow.
2. Swift   from the   north   blow the winds with clouds of   snow.

1. Cold from out the north-land hear the winds of win-ter blow.
2. Swift from out the north-land blow the winds with clouds of   snow.

Liza Jane

1. Come, my love, and go with me, Li'l Li - za Jane,
2-4. I got a house in Bal - ti - more, Li'l Li - za Jane,

Come, my love, and go with me,
Street car runs right by my door, Li'l Li - za Jane,
Brus - sels car - pet on the floor,
Sil - ver door - plate on the door,

O E - li - za, li'l Li - za Jane, O E - li - za, li'l Li - za Jane!

Turn to page 239 for orchestra parts.

The Pie

Traditional   NOTE   Old English Song

A pie sat on the pear tree, A pie sat on the

pear tree, A pie sat on the pear tree, Heigh

A pie sat on the pear tree, Heigh

ho! Heigh ho! Heigh ho! — Then once so mer-ri-ly

ho! Heigh ho! Heigh ho! —

A pie is a magpie.

hopped she, And twice so mer - ri - ly hopped she, Three

times so mer - ri - ly hopped she, Heigh ho! Heigh ho! Heigh ho!

Tippi Canoo

Adapted　　　　　　**NOTE**　　　　**Flemish Sailors' Song**

Lively

1. Hur-rah, hur-ree for　Cap-tain Jones,
2. Hur-rah, hur-ree for　Bo - s'n Peck,　Tip-pi-ca-noo, ca - noh!
3. Hur-rah, hur-ree for　all　our crew,

He　ate　the　meat　and　gave　us　the bones,　He
He　piped　us　out,　we　pol - ished　the　deck,　He
We　sailed　the　sev - en　o - ceans thro'　With

got　the plums and threw us　the stones,
ran　the ship　and made her a wreck,　Tip-pi-ca-noo, ca - noh! —
no　more work than an - y could do.

Sunrise

Adapted   NOTE   **Liszt**

1. The last pale stars are fad - ing Thro'
2. The east - ern stars are glow - ing With

clouds of mist - y gray, While drow - sy earth, still
hues of ros - y light, When o'er the far ho-

sleep - ing, A - waits the dawn of day.
ri - zon, The sun breaks in - to sight.

Turn to page 240 for orchestra parts.

Wake Up, Jacob

Traditional · ROTE · Spiritual

Wake up, Ja - cob, day is a-break-ing, I'm on my way; —

Rhythmic
Descant
H H H H H

O wake up, Ja-cob, day is a-breaking, I'm on my way.

F F F F F F

1. I want to go to heav - en when I die, Do love the Lord,
2. I got some friends on the oth-er shore, Do love the Lord,

H H H H H

I want to go to heav-en when I die, Do love the Lord.
I got some friends on the oth-er shore, Do love the Lord.

F   F   F   F F   F

Clap cupped hands on H; clap open hands sharply on F.

Forest Music

J. W. Beattie NOTE **J. Wolverton**

Slowly

1. Eve - ning winds blow-ing from dark - 'ning sky
2. Ce - dar and pine waft a song to me,

1. From the sky,
2. Song to me,

Sway the great tree - tops to rus-tling lull - a - by.
Join - ing the birch - es in for - est har - mo - ny.

Sway the tree - tops to lull - a - by.
Join - ing birch - es in har - mo - ny.

Rock-a My Soul

Traditional   ROTE   **Spiritual**

Few voices:

1. **2.** *End*

Leader

O rock-a my, O rock-a my soul.

1. See that wom-an all
2. I was blind and

Sway, sway ————

O rock-a my, O rock-a my soul.

Go to the beginning.

dressed so fine, She ain't got Je - sus on her mind. O
could not see, King Je - sus brought the light to me. O

Somebody's Calling My Name

Traditional   NOTE   Spiritual

Moderately slow
Chorus

Hush, hush, some-bod-y's call-ing my name; Hush, hush,

some-bod - y's call - ing my name; Hush, hush,

some-bod - y's call - ing my name; O my Lord, —

End

O my Lord, ——— What shall I do?

(161)

Leader

1. I'm so glad that trou-ble don't last al-ways,
2. I'm so glad that the dev-il can't do me no harm,

I'm so glad that trou-ble don't last al-ways,
I'm so glad that the dev-il can't do me no harm,

I'm so glad that trou-ble don't last al-ways,
I'm so glad that the dev-il can't do me no harm,

Go to the beginning.

O my Lord, — O my Lord, — What shall I do? —
O my Lord, — O my Lord, — What shall I do? —

What a Mornin'

Traditional   NOTE   Spiritual

Slowly
Chorus

My Lord, what a morn-in'; My Lord, what a morn-in';

My Lord, what a morn-in' When the stars be-gin to fall.

Leader

1. You'll hear the trum-pet sound, To wake the na-tions un-der - ground,
2. You'll hear the sin - ner moan, To wake the na-tions un-der - ground,
3. You'll hear the Christ-ian shout, To wake the na-tions un-der - ground,

Chorus

Look-in' to my God's right hand, When the stars be-gin to fall.

Rhythmic descant to be used throughout the song:

Hand clap

Hand clap   *etc.*

Foot stamp

Sally Brown

Traditional   NOTE   Sailor Chantey

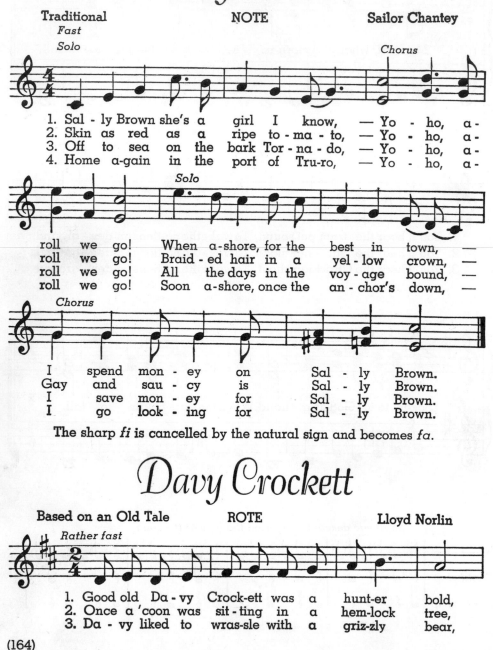

Fast

Solo   *Chorus*

1. Sal - ly Brown she's a girl I know, — Yo - ho, a-
2. Skin as red as a ripe to - ma - to, — Yo - ho, a-
3. Off to sea on the bark Tor - na - do, — Yo - ho, a-
4. Home a-gain in the port of Tru-ro, — Yo - ho, a-

Solo

roll we go! When a-shore, for the best in town, —
roll we go! Braid - ed hair in a yel - low crown, —
roll we go! All the days in the voy - age bound, —
roll we go! Soon a-shore, once the an - chor's down, —

Chorus

I spend mon - ey on Sal - ly Brown.
Gay and sau - cy is Sal - ly Brown.
I save mon - ey for Sal - ly Brown.
I go look - ing for Sal - ly Brown.

The sharp *fi* is cancelled by the natural sign and becomes *fa*.

Davy Crockett

Based on an Old Tale   ROTE   Lloyd Norlin

Rather fast

1. Good old Da - vy Crock-ett was a hunt-er bold,
2. Once a 'coon was sit - ting in a hem-lock tree,
3. Da - vy liked to wras-sle with a griz-zly bear,

Fa - mous wher - ev - er tall tales are told; —
Shout-ed to Da - vy: "Don't shoot at me, —
Trap-ping or shoot-ing did not seem fair; —

With ri - fle al-ways read-y and with sight so keen, —
I know your rep-u - ta-tion, bet-ter save your shot, —
One day he got old Bru-in with a might-y swipe, —

He could fire and hit a crit-ter no one else had seen. —
For I'll hur-ry down and meet you just as soon as not." —
Took him home and taught him how to smoke a corn-cob pipe. —

Chorus

Root - in', toot - in', shoot - in' Da - vy —

Dunked his bread in bear-fat gra-vy, Sea-soned well with

pow-der and ball; Great-est woods-man of them all. —

Find the syncopation in this song.

Flag of Liberty

May W. Ward   NOTE   Grace V. Wilson

With expression

1. Proud-ly flies our flag on high, A-bove the true and brave;
2. Un-der-neath a hun-dred flags, A glo-rious di-a-dem,

Men must fight for what is right, No oth-er way can save;
Those who cher-ish free-dom's cause De-fend the rights of men;

Free-dom's em-blem, Stars and Stripes, Float on! we thrill to see
E-ven those we count our foes Shall change their hearts and see

March-ing men and   o - ver them The flag of lib - er - ty.
Peace can make all   na - tions' flags The flag of lib - er - ty.

Spring's First Song

Ruth Edland   NOTE   Florence Jolley

Brightly

1. Did you ev - er hear a peep - er sing, "Knee deep, knee deep,"
2. Ev - 'ry time I hear a peep - er call, "Knee deep, knee deep,"

His mat-ing call in ear - ly spring, "Knee deep, knee deep?"
I won-der why he sings at all, "Knee deep, knee deep,"

In March he starts his fun - ny song and keeps it up
Per - haps his cho - rus sounds that way from prac - tice on

the whole night long, "Knee deep, knee deep, knee   deep." —
a rain - y day, "Knee deep, knee deep, knee   deep." —

(167)

Come, Gentle Spring

Translated   ROTE   Haydn
From "The Seasons"

Come, gen-tle spring, e-the-real mild-ness, come! —

Come, gen-tle spring, e-the-real mild-ness, come! —

Come! Come! And from her win-t'ry

And from her win-t'ry grave, And from her win-t'ry

growing louder

grave Bid drow-sy na-ture rise. Come,

grave Bid drow-sy na-ture rise. Come, gen-tle

(168)

come, gen - tle spring! — Bid drow-sy na - ture

spring! Bid drow - sy na-ture a - rise, na - ture

rise. Come, gen - tle spring, e - the - real mild-ness,

rise. Come, gen - tle spring, e - the-real mild-ness,

come! — Come! Come! And

come, e - the - real mild - ness, come! And

smil - ing   on our plains de - scend,   O   come,   gen - tle

smil - ing   on our plains de-scend,   O   come,   O   come,

spring,   O come while   mu - sic   wakes   a - round! — O

gen - tle spring, while   mu - sic   wakes   a - round, O come,

p   *growing louder*

come,   O   come,   while   mu - sic   wakes   a-

O come, O   come, O come, while   mu - sic wakes   a-round, While mu - sic wakes a - round.

round, While mu - sic wakes a - round.

Gaelic Lullaby

Unknown   NOTE   Grace V. Wilson

Smoothly

1. Hush, the waves are roll - ing in, White with foam, white with foam;
2. Hush, the winds roar harsh and deep; On they come, on they come;
3. Hush, the rain sweeps o'er the knowes, Where they roam, where they roam;

Fa - ther toils a - mid the din, But Ba - by sleeps at home.
Broth - er seeks the wan - d'ring sheep, But Ba - by sleeps at home.
Sis - ter goes to seek the cows, But Ba - by sleeps at home.

Knowes (nohz) are small round hills.

Bonnie Doon

Robert Burns   ROTE   Scottish Folk Song

Ye   banks   and   braes   o'   bon - nie   Doon,

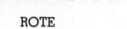

How   can   ye   bloom   sae   fresh   and fair?

How   can   ye   chant,   ye   lit - tle   birds,

And   I   sae   wea - ry,   fu'   o'   care?

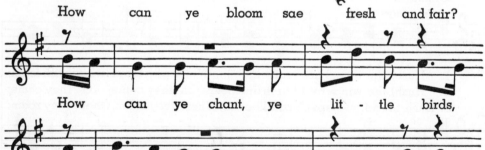

Thou'll   break   my   heart,   thou   war - bling   bird,   That

Hm — —   Hm — —

(172)

wan - tons through the flow - 'ring thorn,

Hm — Hm — —

Hm — Hm —

Ye mind me o' de - part - ed joys,

Hm — — —

De - part - ed nev - er to re - turn.

Western Horizon

G. F. McKay   NOTE   G. F. McKay

1. Far a - way to the west-ern rim,
2. As I look to the west-ern edge,

where the sum - mer day is done, And the light now grows
where the sea and shore-line meet, Where the waves break on

soft and dim from the set - ting sum - mer sun, I
rock - y ledge with an end - less, time - less beat, I

gaze and dream and won - der at all the far-flung light
gaze and wish and pon - der as, o'er the out-stretched plain,

So soon to be hid - den in the peace - ful night.
To the sea I wan - der in dream a - gain.

(175)

An Evening Prayer

William A. Evans   NOTE   William A. Evans

Fa-ther, in Thy keep-ing, Guard-ing me while sleep-ing,

May the an-gels watch o'er me, Ear-nest-ly I pray.

Grant that on a-wak-ing, With the sun-light break-ing,

Kind and help-ful I may be Thro' an - oth - er day.

Killarney

Michael W. Balfe ROTE Michael W. Balfe

Moderately

1. By Kil - lar - ney's lakes and fells, Em - 'rald isles and
2. Mu - sic there for ech - o dwells, Makes each sound a

wind - ing bays, Moun-tain paths and wood-land dells,
har - mo - ny; Man - y - voiced the cho - rus swells,

Mem - 'ry ev - er fond - ly strays; Boun-teous na - ture
Till it faints in ec - sta - sy. With the charm-ful

loves all lands, Beau - ty wan - ders ev - 'ry - where,
tints be - low, Seems the heav'n a - bove to vie,

slower

Foot-prints leaves on man - y strands, But her home is
All rich col - ors that we know Tinge the cloud-wreaths

pp

pure - ly there! An - gels fold their wings and rest
in that sky. Wings of an - gels so might shine,

In that E - den of the West, Beau - ty's home, Kil -
Glanc - ing back soft light di - vine, Beau - ty's home, Kil -

f

lar - ney, Ev - er fair Kil - lar - ney.
lar - ney, Ev - er fair Kil - lar - ney.

March in Three Beats

J. W. Beattie   NOTE   Henry Cowell

Not too fast

3/4

1. The Eng-lish, the French and a lot of folk more
2. That I -rish are odd on their feet is no news,

Go hik - ing a - long with a step two or four;
They find in odd beat e - ven wear on their shoes;

(178)

But if they were care-ful in count-ing the beat,
So when they go hik-ing they count time by three,

They'd change to a three and be eas-y on feet.
With right, left, right, left, right, left, right, left, you see.

When young Pat-rick Kear-ney comes out of Kil-lar-ney
When young Pat-rick Kear-ney goes back to Kil-lar-ney

With Bra-dy and Gra-dy and Ri-ley and Brill,
With Bro-gan and Mo-gan and Kel-ly and Gill,

Mc-Shane and Mc-Con-nell, O'-Rourke and O'-Don-nell,
Mc-Cague and Ma-lo-ney, O'-Keefe and O'-Ro-ney,

They step one, two, three on their march o'er the hill.
They step one, two, three on their march o'er the hill.

Golden Slumbers

Traditional   NOTE   English Folk Song

1. Gold-en slum-bers kiss your eyes, Smiles a-wake you
2. Care is heav-y, there-fore sleep, Moth-er here safe

Sleep, pret-ty loved one, do not cry, And

when you rise; } Sleep, do not cry, ——
watch will keep;

Sleep, pret-ty loved one, do not cry, ——

I will sing a lull-a-by. Lull-a-by,

Lull — a — by, —— Lull-a-by,

Lull — a — by, ——

Lull - a - by, Lull - a - by. —

Lull - a - by, Lull - a - by. —

Lull - a - by, Lull - a - by. —

Twilight

Adapted NOTE **Mozart**

Smoothly, quietly

When the dark-'ning shad - ows fall, o'er the val - ley

When the dark-'ning shad - ows fall, o'er the val - ley

steal - ing, Far - off church bells slow - ly call,

steal - ing, Far - off church bells slow - ly call,

soft their mes-sage peal - ing. Hear the ring - ing,

soft their mes-sage peal - ing.

sing - ing bells, qui - et night the sound fore - tells.

Hear the ring - ing, sing - ing bells, qui - et night the

Ring, ding dong! How sweet their part - ing

sound fore - tells. Ring, ding dong! Their part - ing

song! Round the pleas - ant coun - try - side

song! Round the pleas - ant coun - try - side

shad-ows dark are fall - ing, Ves - per bells at

shad-ows dark are fall - ing, Ves - per bells at

e - ven - tide men to rest are call - ing.

e - ven - tide men to rest are call - ing.

Smiling Spring

Robert Burns ROTE **Old Scottish Tune**

1. The smil-ing spring comes in re-joic-ing, And
flow-'ry spring leads sun-ny sum-mer, And

sur - ly win - ter grim-ly flies; Now crys-tal clear are the
yel - low au - tumn press-es near; Then in his turn comes

fall - ing wa - ters, And bon - nie blue are the
gloom - y win - ter Till smil - ing spring a -

sun-ny skies. Fresh o'er the moun-tain breaks forth the morn-ing, The
gain ap-pears. Thus sea-sons danc-ing, all life ad-vanc-ing, Old

eve-ning gilds the o-cean's swell; All crea-tures joy in the
Time and na-ture their chang-es tell, But nev - er rang - ing,

sun's re-turn - ing, And I re - joice in my Bon - nie Bell!
still un - chang - ing, I a - dore my Bon - nie Bell!

All crea-tures joy in the sun's re-turn - ing, And
But nev - er rang - ing, still un - chang-ing,

I re-joice in my Bon-nie Bell! — 2. The
I a-dore my Bon-nie Bell! —

The Shy Violet

Ruth Edland   ROTE   Spanish Folk Song

Moderately

1. Vi - o - let in the gar-den, Shy - ly your-self you hide
2. Vi - o - let, all the flow-ers Ask you to dance with them,

Far from the oth - er flow - ers, Far from the ros - es' side;
Ask you to spread your pet - als, Ask you to lift your stem;

Think-ing no one will see you, Why do you hide your face,
All of the flow-ers love you, Vi - o - let, show your face,

When all your scent re-veals you, Shows me your hid - ing place?
See where the rose is grow-ing, There is your prop-er place.

(185)

Spring Song

William Griffith   NOTE   J. Wolverton

In swaying rhythm

1. Soft - ly at dawn a whis-per stole   O - ver a green-house
2. Gos - sip-ping on the coun-try-side, Wand-er-ing breez - es

on   the hill,   En - chant - ing   man - y a
soft - ly say   That   God   has   thrown heav'n

ghost-ly hole And   wood-land song with an - cient trill.
o - pen wide And   let the thrush-es   out   to - day.

The Brooklet

Translated from
W. Mueller

ROTE

Schubert

Melody   I   heard a brook - let   mur - mur   a -

heard a brook - let   mur - mur

down its   rock - y   height,   In - to   the val - ley

So   won-drous fresh and   bright,   I

flow - ing.   So   won-drous fresh and bright,   I

(187)

know not how it hap-pened Or who the im-pulse

know not how it hap-pened Or who the im-pulse

Melody

gave, But I must fol-low down-ward, must

gave, But I must fol-low down-ward, must

take my walk-ing stave,

Melody

take my walk-ing stave, But I must fol-low

Melody

Echo diminishes.

p

and I must take my walk-ing stave, But

on - ward, must take my walk-ing stave, But

Melody

pp

I must fol - low on-ward, Must take my walk-ing

p

I must fol - low on - ward, Must take my walk-ing

stave, take my stave, take my stave. —

pp

stave, take my stave, take my stave. —

Alleluia

Isaac Watts

NOTE

Old German Air
Seventeenth Century

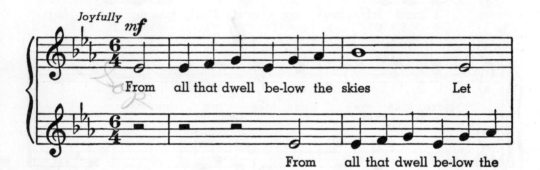

Joyfully *mf*

From all that dwell be-low the skies Let

From all that dwell be-low the

the Cre - a - tor's praise a - rise, Al - le -

skies Let the Cre - a - tor's praise a -

lu - ia! Al - le - lu - ia! Let   the Re-deem-er's name be

rise,   Al - le - lu - ia!   Let

sung   Through   ev - 'ry land, by   ev - 'ry

the   Re-deem-er's   name   be   sung   Through

tongue,   Al - le - lu - ia! Al - le - lu - ia! Al - le-

ev - 'ry   land, by   ev - 'ry tongue!   Al - le - lu - ia! Al - le-

lu - ia!   Al - le - lu - ia! Al - le - lu   -   ia!

lu - ia! Al - le - lu - ia! Al - le - lu   -   ia!

Easter

Isabel Innes NOTE Unknown

Rhythmically

1. The bells in ev-'ry stee-ple chime The joy of East - er - tide,
2. The bells sing out a sto - ry old To wake the sleep-ing earth,

Ding dong ding dong ding ding dong!

O'er crowd-ed cit - y thor-ough-fare And peace-ful country-side.
They tell of tree and leaf and bud, All na-ture's glad re-birth.

Ding dong ding dong ding ding dong!

Turn to page 240 for orchestra parts.

Lilacs in the Rain

Edna Becker NOTE Grace V. Wilson

Moderately

1. Morn-ing glo - ries pink and blue, yel-low daf-fo - dils,
2. Hol - ly-hocks a - long a wall, crim-son ros es bright,

Peach and ap - ple trees in bloom Flam-ing o'er the hills,
Su - mac leaves in ear - ly fall, Fields of dais-ies white,

Pop - pies in their var-ied gowns, Tu-lips down the lane,
Scar-let sag - es by the walk, Gay with flash-ing train,

slower *in time*

All are fair un - til you've seen Li-lacs in the rain.
All are fair un - til you've seen Li-lacs in the rain.

Friendship

Translated NOTE Mozart

Moderately slow

1. Friends are held by a chain for - ev - er,
2. Friends are held by a chain ne'er part - ed,

1. Friends are held by a chain for - ev - er,
2. Friends are held by a chain ne'er part - ed,

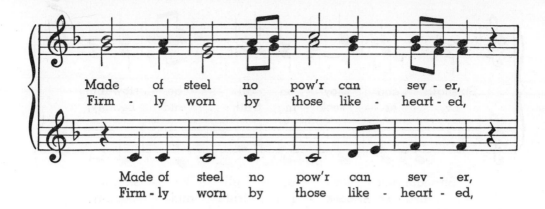

Made of steel no pow'r can sev-er,
Firm-ly worn by those like-heart-ed,

Made of steel no pow'r can sev-er,
Firm-ly worn by those like-heart-ed,

mf

Forged to last a life-time through;
Hand to hand a life-time long;

mf

Forged to last a life-time through;
Hand to hand a life-time long;

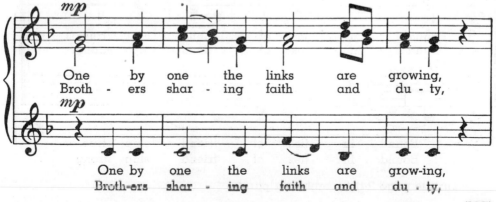

mp

One by one the links are growing,
Broth-ers shar-ing faith and du-ty,

mp

One by one the links are grow-ing,
Broth-ers shar-ing faith and du-ty,

(195)

Strength and joy on all be - stow-ing,
Ev - er seek - ing truth and beau-ty,

Strength and joy on all be - stow-ing,
Ev - er seek - ing truth and beau-ty,

Bound in ties of friend - ship true,
Bound in ties of friend - ship strong,

Bound in ties of friend - ship true,
Bound in ties of friend - ship strong,

mf

Bound in ties of friend - ship true.
Bound in ties of friend - ship strong.

mf

Bound in ties of friend - ship true.
Bound in ties of friend - ship strong.

Turn to page 241 for orchestra parts:

April

Adapted   NOTE   German Folk Song
Arr. by F. B. Cookson

1. The A-pril rain is fall - ing from storm-y clouds on high,
2. The A-pril wind is blow - ing o'er field and mead-ow gray,

1. The rain comes down from storm-y clouds on high,
2. The wind blows on o'er field and mead-ow gray,

In gust - y tor-rent sweep-ing, like some great gi - ant weep - ing,
In might - y cho-rus howl-ing, like some great mon-ster prowl-ing,

Comes sweep - ing,   a gi - ant weep-ing,
Gales howl - ing,   a mon-ster prowl-ing,

The A-pril rain is fall - ing, fall-ing from the sky.
The A-pril wind is blow - ing, blow-ing spring our way.

The A-pril rain is fall -ing from the sky.
The A-pril wind is blow-ing spring our way.

Turn to page 242 for orchestra parts.

Slumber Song

Translated   NOTE   German Folk Song

1. Good night, good night, my own true love, Your weary eye-lids close; The sun has fled the sky above; Sleep now in sweet repose.
2. In dark-'ning grove the night-in-gale Pours forth her sil-ver tone; And in the ear-ly twi-light pale, The moon rides high a-lone.

Lull - a - by, Ah, lull - a - by, Lull - a - by, Ah, lull - a - by.

May an - gels hov - er ev - er near And
The si - lent stars a vig - il keep A -

Lull - a - by,

watch a-round you ly - ing here. Good night, good night, my
bove you safe in slum - ber deep. Good night, good night, my

lull - a - by, Lull - a -

dear - est one, Sleep well, for day is done.
dear - est one, Sleep well, for day is done.

by, Ah, lull - a - by.

The Answer

Paraphrased ROTE Schumann

Lightly

When I walk in the gar-den path thro' rows of pink and

When I walk in the gar-den path thro' rows of pink and

green, To my thoughts comes a

green, thro' rows of pink and green, To my thoughts comes a

ques-tion, a prob-lem un-fore-seen,

ques-tion, a prob - lem all un-fore-seen, A ques-tion and a

A - bove me in the sky a

prob-lem un-fore-seen;

star is faint-ly glow-ing,

How may I shed a kind-ly light, true

When I walk in the gar-den path, the

love be - stow-ing? When I walk in the gar-den path, the

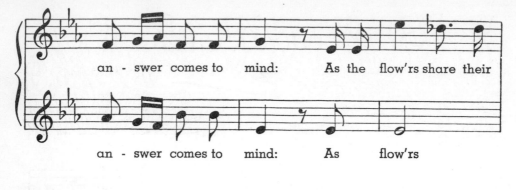

an - swer comes to mind: As the flow'rs share their

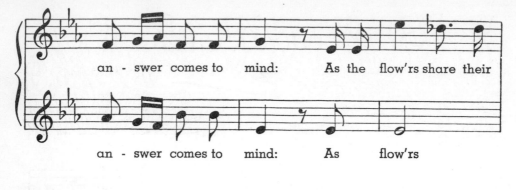

an - swer comes to mind: As flow'rs

beau - ty, Be ev - er true and kind, As the

share, Be tru - ly kind, As

flow'rs share their beau - ty, Be ev - er tru - ly kind.

flow'rs share, Be ev - er tru - ly kind.

Sourwood Mountain

Traditional   ROTE   Southern Folk Song

Fast
Solo

1. Chick- ens   a - crow - ing on   Sour   wood Moun - tain,
2. Rac -coon   he can-ter and the   pos - sum   trot,
3. Jay -bird   a - sit - ting on   hick - 'ry   limb,
4. Gath - er   that game   and   we   won't tar - ry,
5. My   true love   lives   o - ver   the moun - tain,

Chorus

Hey   did - dle dum,   did - dle dum day,

Solo

Get   your   dogs   and   we'll   go   hunt - ing,
Black   cur   wras-sle with   a   hick - 'ry   knot,
My   six-foot   ri - fle   will   sure   get   him,
Got as   much   meat   as   we   can   car - ry,
Few   more   jumps   and   I'll   be   with her,

Chorus

Hey   did - dle dum,   did - dle dum day.

The Erie Canal

Traditional   ROTE   American Folk Song

In walking rhythm

1. I've got a mule, her name is Sal, Fif-teen miles on the
2. We'd bet-ter go our way, old gal, Fif-teen miles on the

E - rie Ca - nal, She's a good old work-er and a
E - rie Ca - nal, 'Cause you bet your life I'd nev-er

good old pal, Fif - teen miles on the E - rie Ca - nal.
part with Sal, Fif - teen miles on the E - rie Ca - nal.

We've hauled some barg - es in our day, Filled with lum-ber,
Get up there, mule, here comes a lock, We'll make Rome 'bout

coal, and hay And we know ev - 'ry inch of the way From
six o' - clock, One more trip and back we'll go,

Al - ba - ny to Buf - fa - lo. —
Right back home to Buf - fa - lo. —

Low bridge! Ev-'ry-bod-y down! Low bridge, for we're go-ing thro' a town;

And you'll al-ways know your neigh-bor, you'll always know your pal

If you've ev-er nav-i-gat-ed on the E-rie Ca-nal. —

The Arkansas Traveler

Walter Purdy   ROTE   **Old American Reel**

In jig time

2/4

1. O   man-y years a-go in   Ar-kan-saw, A
2. One night as Dan was walk-in' out to   play, He
3. Old Dan he tucked his fid-dle un-der chin, He

stran-ger told this sto-ry to my maw; And of-ten is the time she
met a griz-zly stand-in' in the way; He could-n't climb a tree, he
drew the bow, his mu-sic to be-gin; From all the coun-try round the

said to me, "I know it is the truth, cer-tain as can be."
had no gun, He could-n't fly a-way, he was scared to run.
crit-ters ran To join the par-ty made by old fid-dlin' Dan.

Sing the four sixteenth notes (♪♪♪♪) on one beat.

(205)

There was once in the hills quite a mu-sic-mak-ing man,
Said the bear with a roar as he shook a might-y paw,
Pranc-in' out went the 'coon with a lit-tle por-cu-pine,

Known far and wide as Fid-dlin' Dan; He could
"You're Fid-dlin' Dan from Ar-kan-saw; I will
The bear and bob-cat stepped her fine; So they

play ev-'ry jig, he could hol-ler ev-'ry call For
let you a-lone if you'll play a lit-tle tune And
danced all the night ev-'ry reel and ev-'ry set And

cir-cle, square, or reel, he could fid-dle them all.
or-ga-nize a dance in the light of the moon."
some-where in the hills they are danc-in' yet.

Huckleberry Finn

Adapted   **NOTE**   Based on an
American River Song

Quite fast

1. Huck-le-ber-ry Finn and Wat-son's Jim, With no boat or
2. Huck-le-ber-ry Finn and Wat-son's Jim, Drift-ing la-zi-

pleas-ure craft, Vis-it-ing the riv-er for a swim,
ly a-long, Im-i-tat-ing pi-rates bold and grim,

Came up - on a lum - ber raft; Nav-i-gat-or Finn and
Found that some-times things go wrong; Met a pair of ras-cals,

Helms-man Jim Tho't the raft a prop-er boat, Fit-ted with a cab-in
Duke and King, Liv-ing by their wits, you'd say; Neither one could do an

Chorus

snug and trim, Slow-ly down the stream to float. Roll on,
hon - est thing, So our sail-ors ran a - way. Mark three,

Mis - sis-sip-pi Riv-er, Swing-ing past the O - hi - o,
riv-er's get-ting low-er, All hands pull and snatch her down,

Roll on, Mis-sis-sip-pi Riv-er, Slow-ly down to Mex-i-co.
Mark twain, cur-rent mov-ing slow-er, Sweep her down to Mem-phis town.

Counter melody for Chorus

Roll on, roll on, Swing past the O - hi - o;
Mark three, mark three, All pull and snatch her down;

Roll on, roll on, Down to Mex - i - co.
Mark twain, mark twain, Down to Mem - phis town.

The Ohio Canal

J. W. Beattie　　　　　NOTE　　　　　Based on an
Old American Song

Slowly and lazily

1. Up the Cuy-a-ho-ga, far as Ak-ron, —
2. Doz-ing on the deck in pleas-ant sun-shine, —

O-ver locks a-plen-ty to Co-shoc-ton, —
While the hors-es drag a-long the tow-line, —

New-ark, Chil-li-coth-e, and down a-long the Sci-o,
Wak-ing from the dream-ing of car-go we are haul-ing,

Then to Ports-mouth on the broad O-hi-o. —
"Bridge a-head!" I hear some-bod-y call-ing. —

Float her high, boys, — float her low! —

Float her high, float her low,

Through the locks, boys, — ease her slow! —

Through the locks ease her slow!

Al-ways head-ing for the val-ley we'll be see-ing by and by,

To the val - ley by and by,

For we'll keep the boats a-run-ning if we pump Lake E-rie dry!

We'll get there if we pump Lake E-rie dry!

Johnny Appleseed

Isabel Innes   ROTE   Robert Delaney

A pi-o-neer jour-neyed in ear-ly fron-tier days,

Of strange ap-pear-ance and un - com-mon ways. —

He was gen-tle of face, and of kind, friend-ly deed,

This sim-ple old soul known as John-ny Ap-ple - seed.

Thro' for-est and val-ley, by riv - er and plain

He fol-lowed the set-tlers from Fort Du - quesne, —

Second Part

A - long the O - hi - o by raft or ca - noe,

In a rag-ged bur-lap suit with no hat and no shoe.

mf **All** *f*

Far north to Lake E - rie he made a lone trail

With ap-ple-seeds and Bi-ble and a rust - y tin pail. —

First Part
slower

Plant-ing fruit - ful trees was the fan - ci - ful plan,

All

The vis - ion sur - pris - ing of this or -

in time   *Chant, do not sing:*

chard man.

He trav-eled to Mich-i-gan

Drum. Play as the words are chanted.

o - ver the prai-rie and plant-ed his ap-ples wher-

ev - er he'd tar - ry. He had no gun, he

harmed not a crea-ture, For love of na - ture was

his best fea-ture. He begged the fox - es and the birds in the

(212)

tree, "Let my ap-ple seed-lings be!"

Sing:

They heard his plea, the seeds took root,

The ap-ple trees flour-ished and they bore good fruit. —

Now in the spring-time when blos - soms sway, We

think of John - ny and his odd plant-ing way. —

First Part
slower

He was the dream-er to see it all. So

(213)

Star of Peace

Unknown   NOTE   J. E. Gould

The Goat Herders

Translated   NOTE   Spanish Folk Song

Slowly

Peo-ple say that the shep-herds of the goats nev-er dance;
This I know, when the moon is high they frol - ic and prance.

In a cir-cle, round the caul-dron, o - ver em - bers bright
Join-ing hands, they ca - per mad-ly thro' the star - ry night.

faster

Chi - vi - ri - vi ron - do - a - ron - da - lay, chi - vi - ri - vi

slower

ron - do - a - ron - da - lay, There they dance till break of

day, Chi - vi - ri - vi ron - do - a - ron - da - lay!

(215)

The Hunter

Adapted   NOTE   Bavarian Folk Song

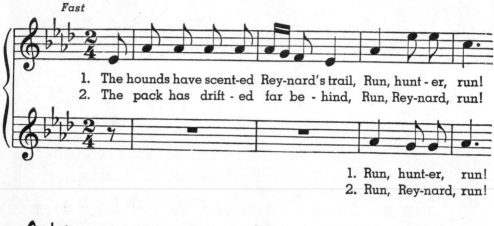

Fast

1. The hounds have scent-ed Rey-nard's trail, Run, hunt-er, run!
2. The pack has drift-ed far be-hind, Run, Rey-nard, run!

1. Run, hunt-er, run!
2. Run, Rey-nard, run!

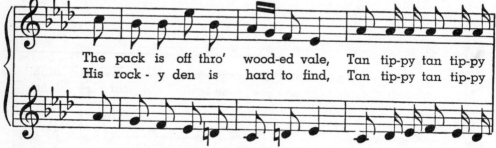

The pack is off thro' wood-ed vale, Tan tip-py tan tip-py
His rock-y den is hard to find, Tan tip-py tan tip-py

Tan tan tan, Now can-ter, can-ter, can-ter o'er the hedg-es'bound!
Tan tan tan, Now hur-ry, hur-ry, hur-ry thro' the coun-try-side!

O hunt-er, quick-ly run a - long the frost-y ground!
O Rey-nard, quick-ly run, from cru-el hunt-ers hide!

Run, run, run a - long the frost-y ground!
Run, run, run, from cru-el hunt-ers hide!

In Bahia

Adapted   NOTE   Brazilian Folk Song
Arr. by H. Villa-Lobos

Lightly

La la la la la la la la la la la la la la

la la la. 1. In Ba - hi - a town, town, town, town,

In Ba - hi - a far a - way the co - co-nuts fall down.

2. Up Bahia's height climb, climb, climb,
Up Bahia's height so steep to ride costs half a dime.

3. On Bahia's breeze ring, ding, ding,
On Bahia's gentle breeze the church bells loudly ring.

Verses to this melody, which is one of the most popular in Latin America, are often improvised, usually in a nonsensical vein. Bahia (bah-ee-yah) was once the capital of Brazil. In Portuguese the song is called "Na Baia tem." Turn to page 242 for orchestra parts.

The Shepherdess

Translated   ROTE   Chilean Tonada

Smoothly, moderately fast

1. One morn - ing as day was dawn - ing   Far
2. The shep - herd - ess held a sto - ry,   Her

o - ver the wide ho - ri - zon,   A mu - si - cal voice re-
eyes on the flock not keep - ing,   And as she was read - ing

sound - ing   Came ech - o - ing down the moun - tain;
slow - ly   She nod-ded and fell a - sleep - ing;

A shep - herd - ess now ap - pear - ing   In
While o - ver the wood and mead - ow   The

wool-en and skin ap - par - el   Was heard in a car - ol
shep-herd-ess' sheep were wan - d'ring, From un - der the lau - rels'

cheer - ing   While seat - ed be-neath the lau - rel. —
shad - ow   The same lit - tle song was sound - ing. —

"How love-ly the rose, the car-na-tion of red, More love-ly the dah-lia just show-ing her head! O look on me not, my dear one, If you like some-one in-stead!" —

The Little Sailboat

Translated   NOTE   Panamanian Folk Song

Lightly

1. Long years a-go there was a lit-tle sail-boat, —

Long years a-go there was a lit-tle sail-boat, —

Long years a-go there was a lit-tle sail-boat, —

So ver-y small it could not sail a-way from shore.

2. The weeks went one and two and three and four and
3. Now if my song has not been

five, six, sev'n in pass - ing, — The weeks went
long e -nough to please you, — Now if my

one and two and three and four and five, six, sev'n in
song has not been long e -nough to

pass - ing, — The weeks went one and two and three and four and
please you, — Now if my song has not been

five, six, sev'n in pass - ing,— And the prov-en - der,
long e -nough to please you,— We'll be-gin a - gain,

and the prov-en - der, and the prov - en - der ran out.
we'll be - gin a - gain, and we'll sing it all once more.

Flying Down to Rio

Adapted   NOTE   Brazilian Game Song

1. If of - fered an - y trans - por - ta - tion to the
2. I go so fast by a - vi - a - tion, soon I'm

place where I would go, The best of all is a - vi -
where I want to be: Bra - zil, that fas - ci - nat - ing

a - tion 'cross the Gulf of Mex - i - co,
na - tion, love - ly Ri - o by the sea,

By the Car - ib - be - an, O - ver Puer - to Ri - co,
'Round the Cor - co - va - da, Head - ing for an is - land

Com-ing down in Trin-i-dad once more, O'er the three Gui-a-nas,
Made for land-ing in a calm, blue bay; Meet-ing man-y peo-ple,

On to old Re - ci - fe, Now to hap-py old San Sal - va - dor.
Play-ing on the beach-es, What a cit - y for a hol - i - day!

The Little Jar

Translated from
Daniel de la Vega

ROTE

Adolfo Allende

Very slowly

Made of burn-ing earth so mean - ly, My lit - tle jar stands se -
Faith - ful lit - tle jar there show - ing, Red as the bright em - bers

rene - ly, All brown as the peo - ple far off in Chi - le,
glow - ing, A clus - ter of fra - grant blos-soms of Christ-mas,

End

Far off in Chi - le.
Crim-son car - na - tions.

Be - neath the lin-den tree

state - ly Your grace-ful, del - i - cate bod - y Re - ceives the

1.

fresh-en-ing wa - ter, the wa - ter blue from the foun - tain.

2.

Go to the beginning.

Be - wa - ter blue from the foun - tain.

Garden Melody

Adapted ROTE **Schumann**

Not too slowly

Pale blue, in clus-ters grow — ing, Del-phin-i-um

blos — soms are grace-ful-ly blow — ing, While close be-

side nod the crim-son ros — es, Whose del-i-cate

o-dors per-vade the air, Scent-ing all the gar-den with their

fra-grance fair. There, as the winds car-ry per-fume

From pet-als of crim-son and blue, Thro' my mem-'ry's

gar-den come re-turn-ing Friend-ships ten-der and true.

Out Walking

Paraphrased   ROTE   Franz Abt

In marked rhythm

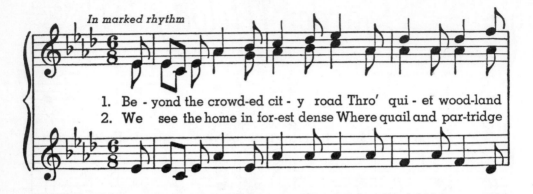

1. Be - yond the crowd-ed cit - y road Thro' qui - et wood-land
2. We see the home in for-est dense Where quail and par-tridge

ways, — We fol - low stream or thorn - y path In
nest, — Where bird and beast at close of day May

pleas - ant sum - mer days;   A - long a shad - y
find a place to rest;   At last we reach a

(224)

coun - try lane Be - side a field of gold - en grain, A-
sand - y pool And learn to swim in wa - ter cool, A

cross a grass - y plain. Heigh ho, a - hik-ing we go.
pleas-ant kind of school. Heigh ho, a - hik-ing we go.

Chorus

Heigh ho, heigh ho, tra la la la la, Heigh ho, heigh ho,

tra la la la la. Heigh ho! Heigh ho!

Heigh ho! — Heigh ho! — Heigh ho!

Tra la la la la la la. Heigh ho! Heigh

Heigh ho! — Heigh ho!

ho! — Heigh ho, a - hik - ing we go.

— Heigh ho!

God, Be Our Guide

Translated   NOTE   Franz Abt

Reverently

1. God, be our Guide, Thy help is sure, In
2. Work that we pur - pose ev - 'ry hour Will

Thee our hope shall rest se - cure, Thy
pros - per on - ly through Thy pow'r, Our

gradually louder

strength a - lone suc - cess can bring; This
souls Thy gra - cious pres - ence seek; With

pray'r from ev - 'ry heart shall spring:
joy - ful lips this pray'r we speak:

God, be our Guide; God, be our Guide.
God, be our Guide; God, be our Guide.

(227)

Grace Before Meat

J. W. Beattie   NOTE   T. Tapper

Thou, Who send-eth all things good, Rai-ment, shel-ter,

drink, and food, Be a - mong us gath-ered here,

Friend and neigh-bor, fam - 'ly dear; On this gift of

bread and meat Send Thy bless-ing ere we eat.

The Star-Spangled Banner

Francis Scott Key   ROTE   John Stafford Smith

Moderately

1. Oh,— say, can you see,— by the dawn's ear - ly
2. On the shore, dim - ly seen— thro' the mists of the
3. Oh,— thus be it ev - er when— free - men shall

light, What so proud - ly we hailed at the twi-light's last
deep; Where the foe's haugh-ty host in dread si - lence re-
stand Be - tween their lov'd homes and the war's des - o-

gleam - ing, Whose broad stripes and bright stars, thro' the
pos - es, What is that which the breeze, o'er the
la - tion! Blest with vic - t'ry and peace, may the

per - il - ous fight, O'er the ram - parts we watched were so
tow - er - ing steep, As it fit - ful - ly blows, half con-
Heav'n - res-cued land Praise the Pow'r that hath made and pre-

gal - lant - ly stream-ing? And the rock - et's red glare, the bombs
ceals, half dis - clos - es? Now it catch-es the gleam of the
served us a na - tion! Then— con - quer we must, when our

burst-ing in air, Gave— proof thro' the night— that our
morn-ing's first beam, In full glo - ry re - flect -ed now—
cause it is just, And— this be our mot - to: "In—

flag was still there. Oh,— say, does that
shines on the stream. 'Tis the Star - Span - gled
God is our Trust." And the Star - Span - gled

Star - Span - gled Ban - ner yet wave—— O'er the
Ban - ner, Oh, long may it wave—— O'er the
Ban - ner in tri - umph shall wave—— O'er the

land—— of the free and the home of the brave?
land—— of the free and the home of the brave!
land—— of the free and the home of the brave.

AMERICA
Key of G

1. My country, 'tis of thee.
   Sweet land of liberty,
   Of thee I sing;
   Land where my fathers died!
   Land of the Pilgrims' pride,
   From ev'ry mountain side,
   Let freedom ring!

2. My native country, thee,
   Land of the noble free,
   Thy name I love;
   I love thy rocks and rills,
   Thy woods and templed hills,
   My heart with rapture thrills
   Like that above.

3. Let music swell the breeze,
   And ring from all the trees
   Sweet freedom's song;
   Let mortal tongues awake,
   Let all that breathe partake,
   Let rocks their silence break,
   The sound prolong!

4. Our fathers' God, to Thee,
   Author of liberty,
   To Thee we sing;
   Long may our land be bright
   With freedom's holy light;
   Protect us by Thy might,
   Great God, our King.

—Samuel Francis Smith

DIXIE
Key of C

1. I wish I was in the land of cotton,
   Old times there are not forgotten,
   Look away! Look away! Look away! Dixie
   Land!
   In Dixie Land where I was born in
   Early on one frosty morning,
   Look away! Look away! Look away! Dixie
   Land!

2. There's buckwheat cakes and Injun batter,
   Makes you fat or a little fatter,
   Look away! Look away! Look away! Dixie
   Land!
   Then hoe it down and scratch your gravel,
   To Dixie Land I'm bound to travel,
   Look away! Look away! Look away! Dixie
   Land!

Refrain:

Then I wish I was in Dixie, Hooray! Hooray!
In Dixie Land I'll take my stand
To live and die in Dixie!
Away, away, away down South in Dixie!
Away, away, away down South in Dixie!

—Daniel D. Emmett

BATTLE HYMN OF THE REPUBLIC
Key of B flat

1. Mine eyes have seen the glory
   Of the coming of the Lord;
   He is trampling out the vintage
   Where the grapes of wrath are stored;
   He hath loosed the fateful lightning
   Of His terrible swift sword;
   His truth is marching on.

2. He has sounded forth the trumpet
   That shall never call retreat;
   He is sifting out the hearts of men
   Before the judgment seat;
   Oh, be swift, my soul, to answer Him;
   Be jubilant, my feet!
   Our God is marching on.

3. In the beauty of the lilies
   Christ was born across the sea,
   With a glory in His bosom
   That transfigures you and me;
   As He died to make men holy,
   Let us die to make men free
   While God is marching on.

Refrain:

Glory, glory! Hallelujah!
Glory, glory! Hallelujah!
Glory, glory! Hallelujah!
His truth is marching on!

—Julia Ward Howe

AMERICA THE BEAUTIFUL
Key of C

1. O beautiful for spacious skies,
   For amber waves of grain,
   For purple mountain majesties
   Above the fruited plain!
   America, America!
   God shed His grace on thee,
   And crown thy good with brotherhood
   From sea to shining sea!

2. O beautiful for pilgrim feet
   Whose stern impassioned stress
   A thoroughfare for freedom beat
   Across the wilderness!
   America, America!
   God mend thine ev'ry flaw,
   Confirm thy soul in self-control,
   Thy liberty in law!

3. O beautiful for heroes proved
   In liberating strife,
   Who more than self their country loved,
   And mercy more than life!
   America, America!
   May God thy gold refine,
   Till all success be nobleness,
   And ev'ry gain divine!

4. O beautiful for patriot dream
   That sees beyond the years
   Thine alabaster cities gleam
   Undimmed by human tears!
   America, America!
   God shed His grace on thee,
   And crown thy good with brotherhood
   From sea to shining sea!

—Katharine Lee Bates

COLUMBIA, THE GEM OF THE OCEAN
Key of G

1. O Columbia, the gem of the ocean,
   The home of the brave and the free,
   The shrine of each patriot's devotion,
   A world offers homage to thee!
   Thy mandates make heroes assemble
   When Liberty's form stands in view;
   Thy banners make tyranny tremble
   When borne by the red, white, and blue!
   When borne by the red, white, and blue,
   When borne by the red, white, and blue,
   Thy banners make tyranny tremble
   When borne by the red, white, and blue!

2. When war winged its wide desolation
   And threatened the land to deform,
   The ark then of freedom's foundation,
   Columbia, rode safe through the storm;
   With the garlands of vict'ry about her
   When so proudly she bore her brave crew,
   With her flag proudly floating before her,
   The boast of the red, white, and blue!
   The boast of the red, white, and blue,
   The boast of the red, white, and blue,
   With her flag proudly floating before her,
   The boast of the red, white, and blue!

3. The star-spangled banner bring hither,
   O'er Columbia's true sons let it wave;
   May the wreaths they have won never wither,
   Nor its stars cease to shine on the brave;
   May the service united ne'er sever
   But hold to their colors so true;
   The Army and Navy forever!
   Three cheers for the red, white, and blue!
   Three cheers for the red, white, and blue,
   Three cheers for the red, white, and blue,
   The Army and Navy forever!
   Three cheers for the red, white, and blue!

—David T. Shaw

Orchestrations

There may be boys and girls in your class or school who play band and orchestral instruments. You can sing and play together even though there are but one or two players. Here are some orchestrations of songs you have learned.

Fairest Lord Jesus

Violins and flutes play the voice parts on page 14.

B-flat cornets and trumpets play:

Cello and trombones play:

Dandelion

Violins and flutes play the voice parts on page 27.

B-flat cornets and trumpets play:

Cello and trombones play:

Faith of Our Fathers

Violins and flutes play the voice parts on page 91
B-flat cornets and trumpets play:

Cello and trombones play:

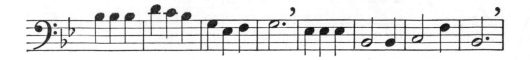

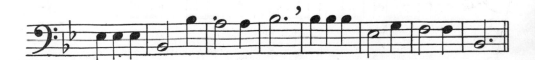

The Troika

Violins and flutes play the voice part on page 134.

B-flat cornets and trumpets play:

Cello and trombones play:

Triangles and sleigh bells play:

Triangle

Bells

Woodblocks play:

My Island

Violins and flutes play the voice parts on page 119.

B-flat cornets and trumpets play:

Cello and trombones play:

Song for Freedom

Violins and flutes play the voice parts on page 132.

B-flat cornets and trumpets play:

Cello and trombones play:

Lovely Meadows

Violins and flutes play the voice parts on page 144.

B-flat cornets and trumpets play:

Cello and trombones play:

Liza Jane

Violins and flutes play the voice parts on page 154.

B-flat cornets and trumpets play:

Cello and trombones play:

Sunrise

Violins and flutes play the voice parts on page 157.
B-flat cornets and trumpets play:

Cello and trombones play:

Easter

Violins and flutes play the voice parts on page 193.
B-flat cornets and trumpets play:

Cello and trombones play:

Friendship

Violins and flutes play the voice parts on page 194.

B-flat cornets and trumpets play:

Cello and trombones play:

April

Violins and flutes play the voice parts on page 197.
B-flat cornets and trumpets play:

Cello and trombones play:

In Bahia

Violins and flutes play the voice parts on page 217.
B-flat cornets and trumpets play:

Cello and trombones play:

Classified Index

(245)

Index of Songs